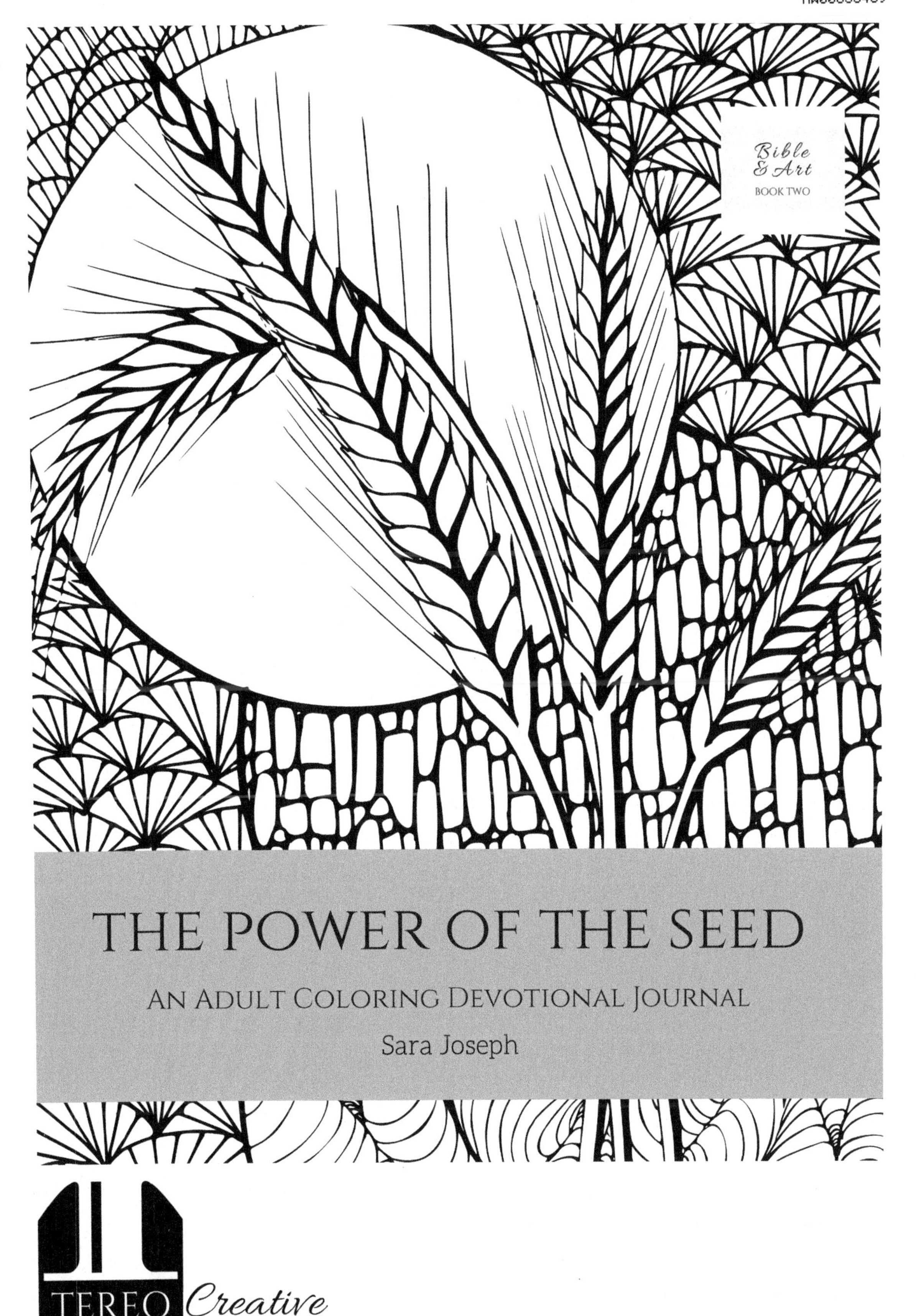

TEREO Creative
FORT WORTH, TEXAS
www.christian-artist-resource.com

THE POWER OF THE SEED

An Adult Coloring Devotional Journal

Bible & Art Series: Book Two

Author Website: www.christian-artist-resource.com

Email: sarajoseph@christian-artist-resource.com

ISBN 978-0-9973673-2-4 (Paperback)

ISBN 978-0-9973673-3-1 (Hardback)

This book is dedicated to God, my Father,
and to my Savior and Lord, Jesus Christ,
the supplier of seed to the sower.
His words bring life to whosoever will believe.

It is His will that we sow generously,
reap abundantly, and increase continually
by the power of the most dynamic seed on earth,
the seed of God's Word.

This Journal Belongs To:

____

Begun On

____

Completed On

____

"Now He who supplies seed to the sower and bread for food will supply and multiply your seed for sowing and increase the harvest of your righteousness."
2 Corinthians 9:10

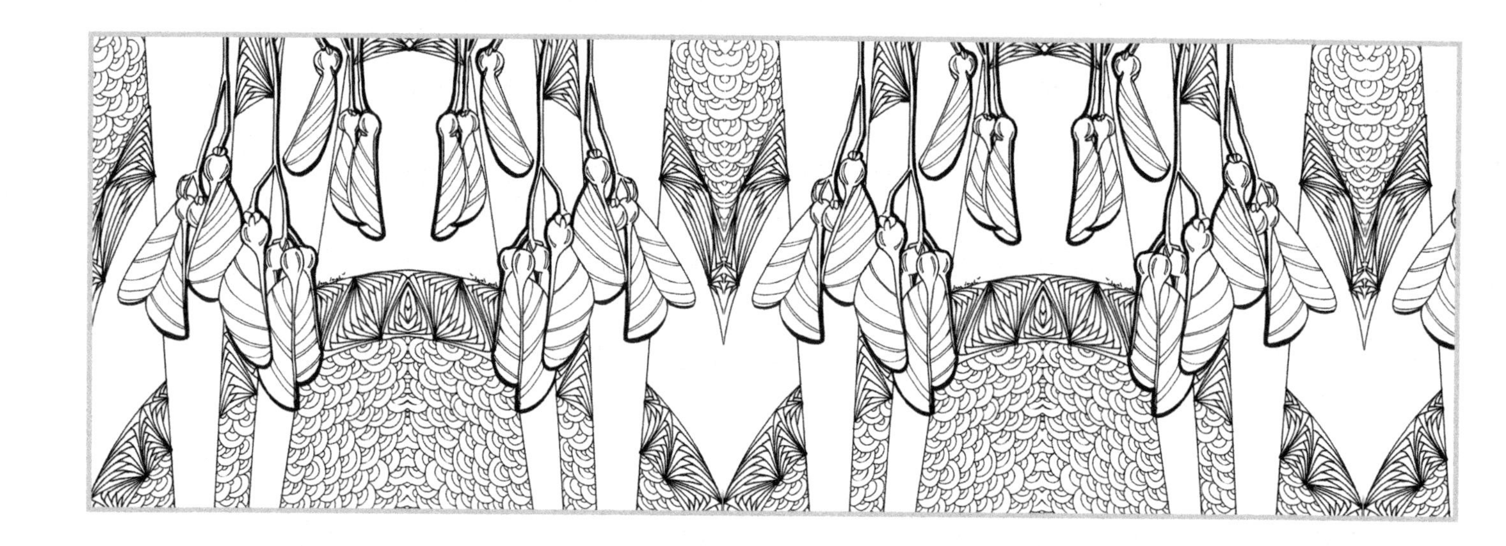

Table of Contents

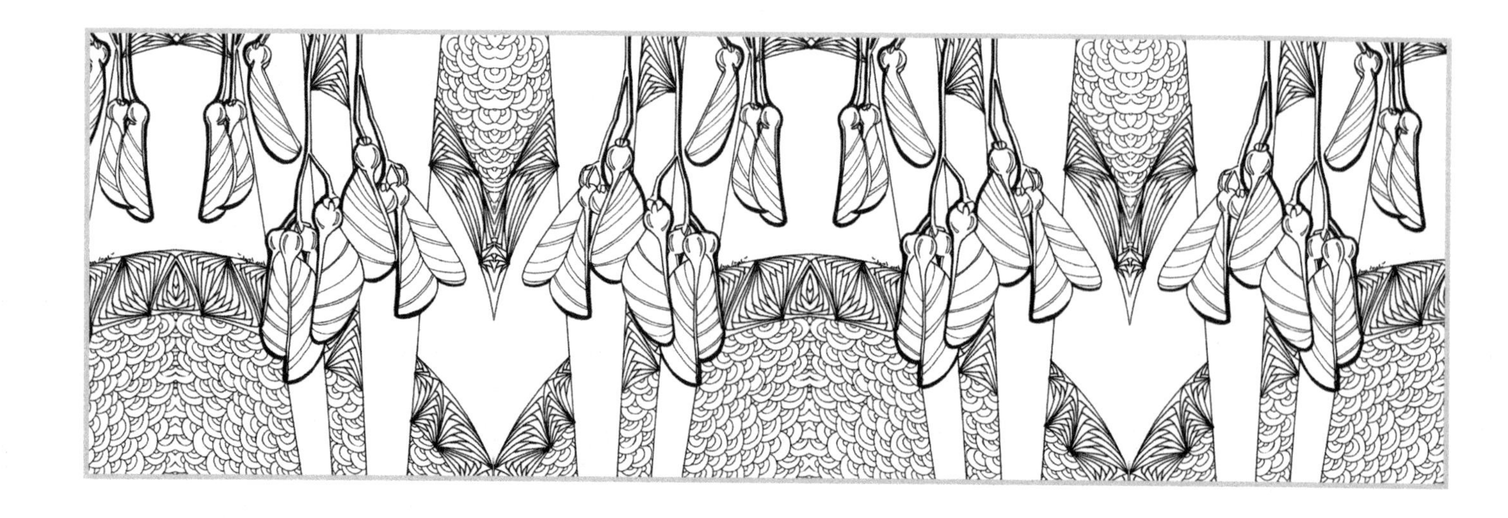

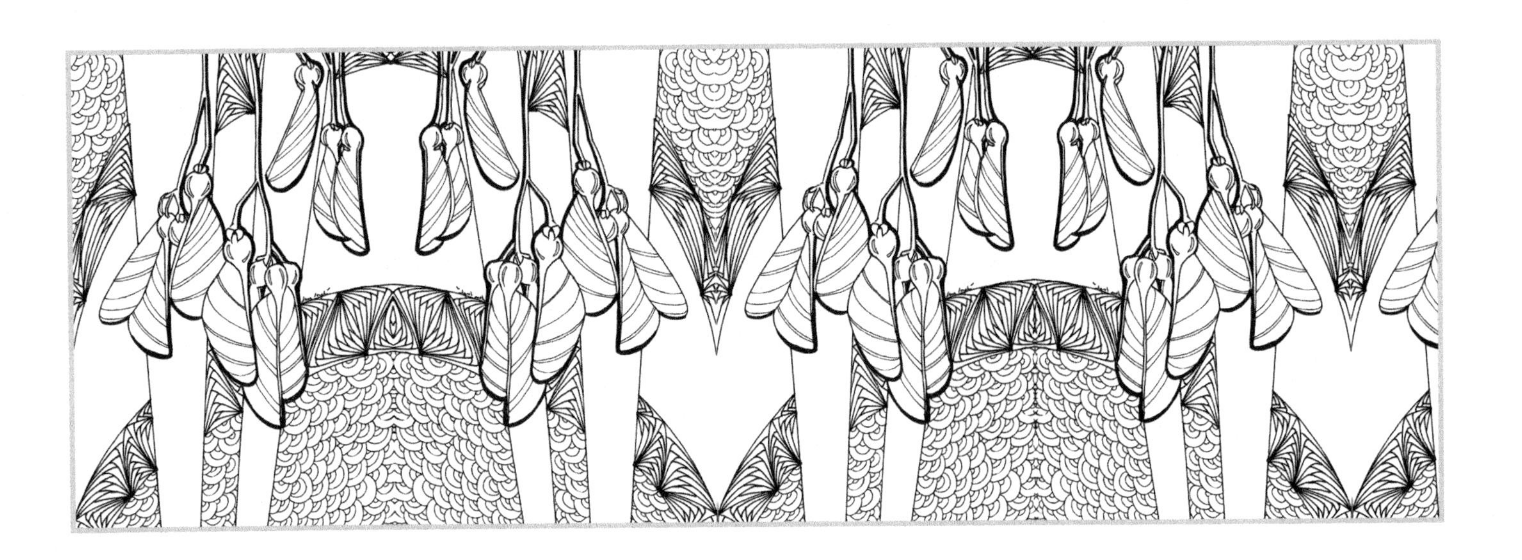

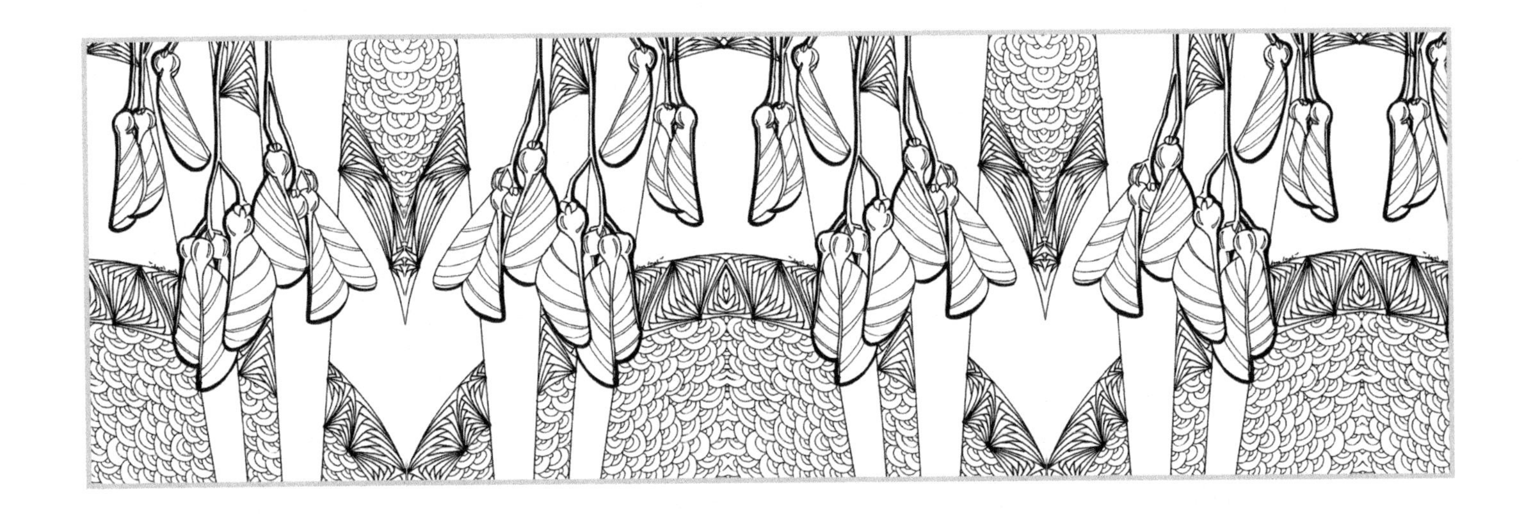

Make the Most of Your Journal

Quiet time with Jesus, the Bible, and a journal is precious. There is no better way to be renewed and strengthened. The purpose of this journal is to mediate on God's Word while engaged in the calming creativity of coloring.

Responding to the prompts, reading the poetry, and contemplating the Scriptures while coloring will help you absorb God's Holy Word. Ask Him questions, journal His responses and your thoughts; plenty of room has been provided for your musings here. His Holy Spirit has promised to guide you into all truth. Expect to be guided.

The prompts I've included in some pages are those I asked myself when I contemplated these verses. Your responses to them will be different from mine, based on your unique life experience. Be honest and document your journey to understanding.

Each of the ink drawings in this book is a painstaking labor of love. Unlike the computer-generated drawings of other coloring books, these hand-drawn images bear the imperfections of human endeavor. Please ignore ink that overstepped its bounds and look kindly upon any wobbly lines that you may spot. They are reflective of my flawed human condition. I yearn and strive for perfection, as I'm sure you do, and consistently fall short of it. The occasional errant streak of ink on paper only warms me to thoughts of my awesome God, who sent His perfect Son for flawed me! Somehow He loves each one of us so much that He corrects our errors, picks us up when we stumble, and urges us on in our journey to perfection.

Therefore when you color a page and the result does not look as you envisioned it, be gentle with yourself. Treasure the process, since by it you will surely grow.

Before You Color

These prayerfully created drawings are the fruit of my lingering reflection on the Scriptures in this journal. As you fill in the colors while meditating on the verses, you will learn much. I promise you that you will receive insight for your specific needs and challenges. Act upon all that you are taught, and your life will certainly never be the same!

Some things to think about before you begin:

This book is less about coloring and more about communing with God and learning from Him.

Although this is a journal, its pages are deliberately not dated. So don't feel guilty if you miss a day; there are no appointments to keep. You choose the time and place, and add a date to help you reminisce one day in the future. The words you commit to paper will cause you to marvel at changes only He could have wrought in you!

Welcome the Lord's presence whenever you sit down to this journal, and fill its pages with whatever He teaches you. There is plenty of room for color, thoughts, insights, and yes, dates, recorded without guilt.

Don't allow the familiarity of these sacred words to lull you into complacency. God can reveal insights you never knew existed. He will ensure that these verses are pertinent to you if you come before Him in faith, expectantly.

Color with colored pencils. Prismacolor pencils are recommended. They come in a wide variety of luscious colors in artist-grade options like Soft Core, Verithin®, Art Stix®, and others like these. Softer than other coloring pencils, they require less pressure and will reward your efforts with vivid, even colors. They are consequently more expensive than other brands. The results are well worth the difference in cost. This is a sacred journey, so I encourage you to bring excellence to every aspect of it. The choice, however, is yours to make.

Gel pens and markers are not a good idea, because they will bleed to the page below. If you just can't help yourself, put a sturdy piece of cardboard under your page to absorb the excess ink and protect the pages below. The back of each drawing has deliberately been left blank for this reason. Make sure you use a light touch when using pens; otherwise ink-sodden paper can tear. This paper is best suited to pencils.

It may be tempting to remove a page that you're really thrilled about in order to frame it or to grace your refrigerator with it. Please don't do that. Removing pages would cause the journal to lack vital information about your growth and transformation. I deliberately did not include perforations because I know that you will be too pleased with the journey to deface a mile marker on the way. I pray that your complete journal becomes a record so precious that you will prize it in its entirety!

You do not have to color every little space if that is overwhelming to you. Look for the larger shapes and unify the colors in those. If, on the other hand, you find the little spaces fascinating, think of each coloring page as you would a panel of stained glass. Select your favorite colors, experiment, play, and enjoy coloring the drawings in this book. Visit www.amazon.com and search for *The Power of the Seed: An Adult Coloring Devotional Journal* to be inspired by the creativity of others who have colored these same pages.

Above all, keep the verses in mind as you color. May they whisper their truths to transform your life!

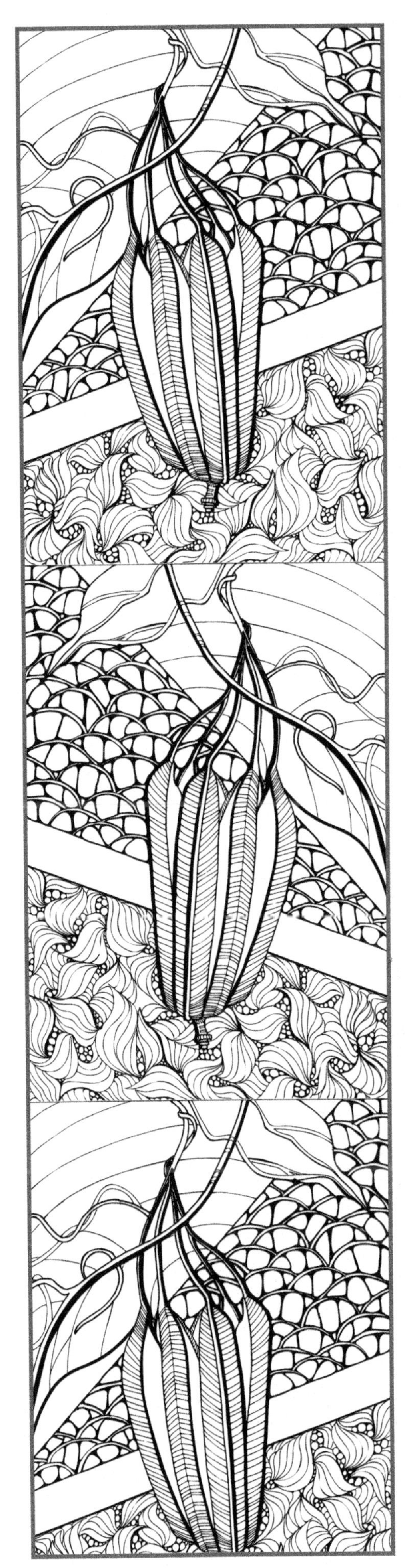

The Power of the Seed

> *"Sow your seed in the morning*
> *and do not be idle in the evening,*
> *for you do not know*
> *whether morning or evening sowing will succeed,*
> *or whether both of them alike will be good."*
> *Ecclesiastes 11:6*

Look down. If you're not standing on anything man-made, the dirt beneath your feet hides something phenomenal—seeds, hundreds and hundreds of them! Often nondescript and microscopic, they possess a power that is easily overlooked. We trample upon them unaware of their potential. Drifting in the wind, sometimes causing you to sneeze, they are designed to carry gardens from region to region. These delivery packages of color and nourishment from the Creator are a vivid metaphor for a spiritual principle that runs all through the Bible. Don't be fooled by the simplicity of seeds; the truths they reveal will, if applied, transform your life forever!

The drawings in this journal are fanciful interpretations of real seeds. I've taken the liberty of exercising some measure of artistic license. My goal was not necessarily to depict seeds exactly as they exist in nature, but rather to offer you opportunities for imaginative coloring while thinking upon biblical concepts. Writing your thoughts and prayers in the journal pages along with coloring will create a precious record of your journey of growth.

The sheer variety and beauty of seeds that I discovered while researching for this book was mind-boggling, giving me plenty of inspiration for these drawings. There may be somewhere between four hundred thousand to a million types of seed-bearing plants. It stretches my math ability to grasp just how many fruits with even more seeds those would produce! If you are bored, cut open a tomato and count its seeds. I guarantee that it will contain more seeds in its juicy flesh than your best estimate.

All seeds exist with one purpose—to reproduce and multiply. In them is concealed the essence of a potential that is breathtaking! Forget about quantifying that power; just concede that it exists.

Studying how best to utilize the principles taught by Jesus, using the humble seed as a metaphor and harnessing its power, is the purpose of this coloring devotional journal.

"For as the rain and the snow come down from heaven,
And do not return there without watering the earth
And making it bear and sprout,
And furnishing seed to the sower and bread to the eater;
So will My word be which goes forth from My mouth;
It will not return to Me empty,
Without accomplishing what I desire,
And without succeeding in the matter for which I sent it."
Isaiah 55: 10-11

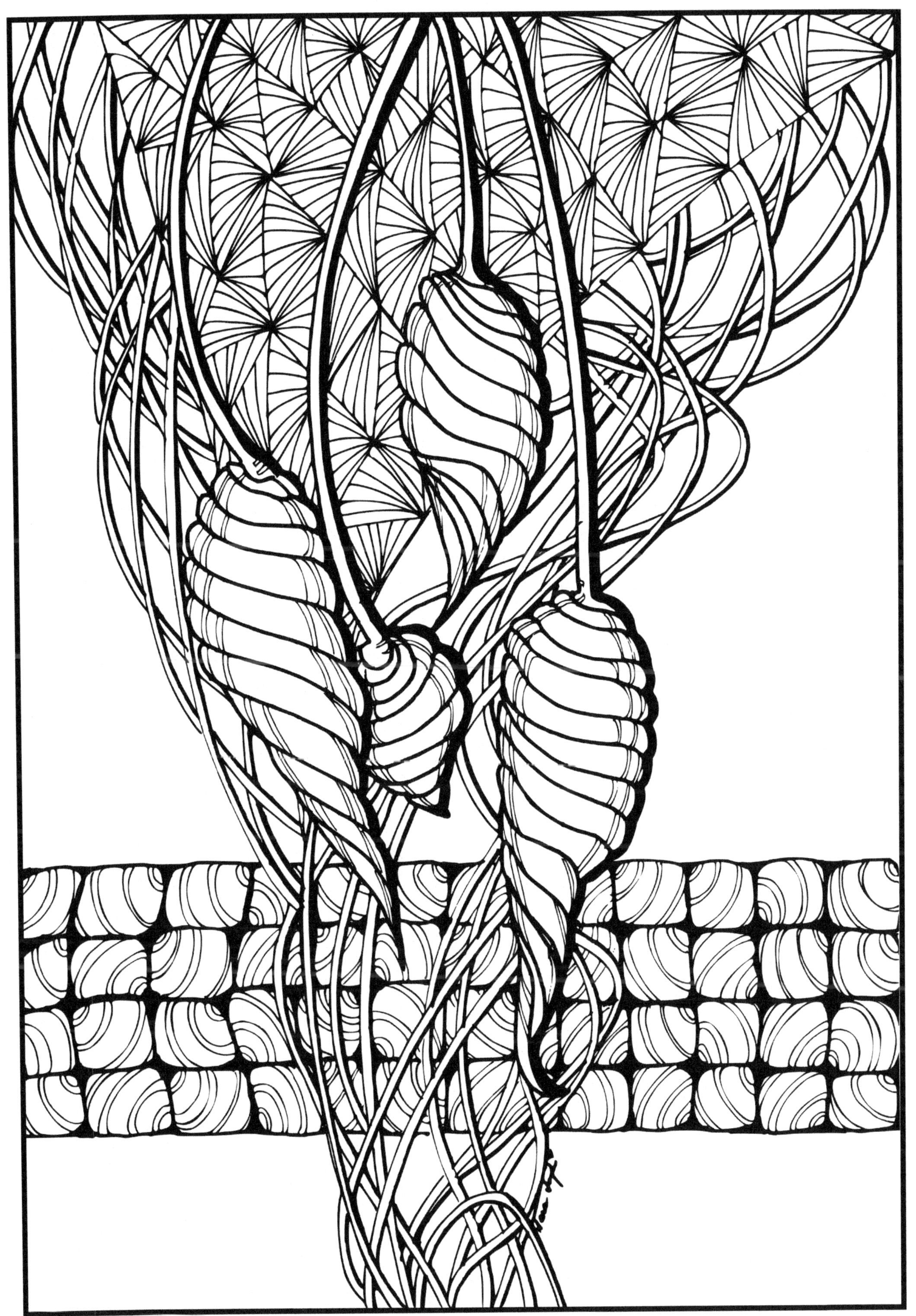

The Quest

> ***"So will My word be which goes forth from My mouth;***
> ***It will not return to Me empty,***
> ***Without accomplishing what I desire,***
> ***And without succeeding in the matter for which I sent it."***
> ***Isaiah 55:11***

Are you stuck in a seemingly endless cycle of apathy, unable to break through? Do you have the nagging sense that there is much to life that is just out of reach, yet you are unable to articulate it? You are not alone. In our fallen state we intuitively seek for something lost—a forgotten world that once was. Stumbling toward a destination we struggle to define, we plunge headlong into the pressing needs of each day and feel the frustration of hopes dashed and dreams unrealized.

The good news is that we can, and must, find our way to that which we sense exists—an exciting, vibrant reality that pulsates with life. There, dreams are not only realized but replaced continually, each more impossible than the ones before, dreams which repeatedly become reality—somewhere Jesus calls the kingdom of heaven! Under His governance we learn to think His thoughts and become trained in His ways. The more readily we yield, despite how alien His ways may seem to us at first, the faster this immensely fruitful kingdom of heaven unfolds in surprising and unusual ways.

Let us therefore humbly acknowledge our limitations and surrender to His awesome power. He will reveal the nuances of this kingdom as it is found in His Word, the Bible. Taking to heart what He teaches us is our first toddling step toward a life that is thrilling beyond measure.

Purpose that no matter how unusual the principles of this kingdom appear, you will get to work applying them. Learn and put into practice every lesson you learn about seeds—sowing, reaping, and sowing again.

In the next pages write out your commitment to set aside all you think you know about His kingdom as a prayer. Now invite Jesus to teach you as you journal and color your way through these pages.

Writing in your own words is powerful; it makes your purpose concrete, notifies heaven of your desire to follow Him, and leaves a record of your journey.

It is also immensely gratifying to revisit a journal years later. You will delight in the tangible record that you now have of God's unfailing faithfulness. If you are open and honest with the questions, challenges, and accompanying emotions of this season in your life, then your future self will marvel at the changes God wrought in you, through you, and around you. This is a worthwhile adventure!

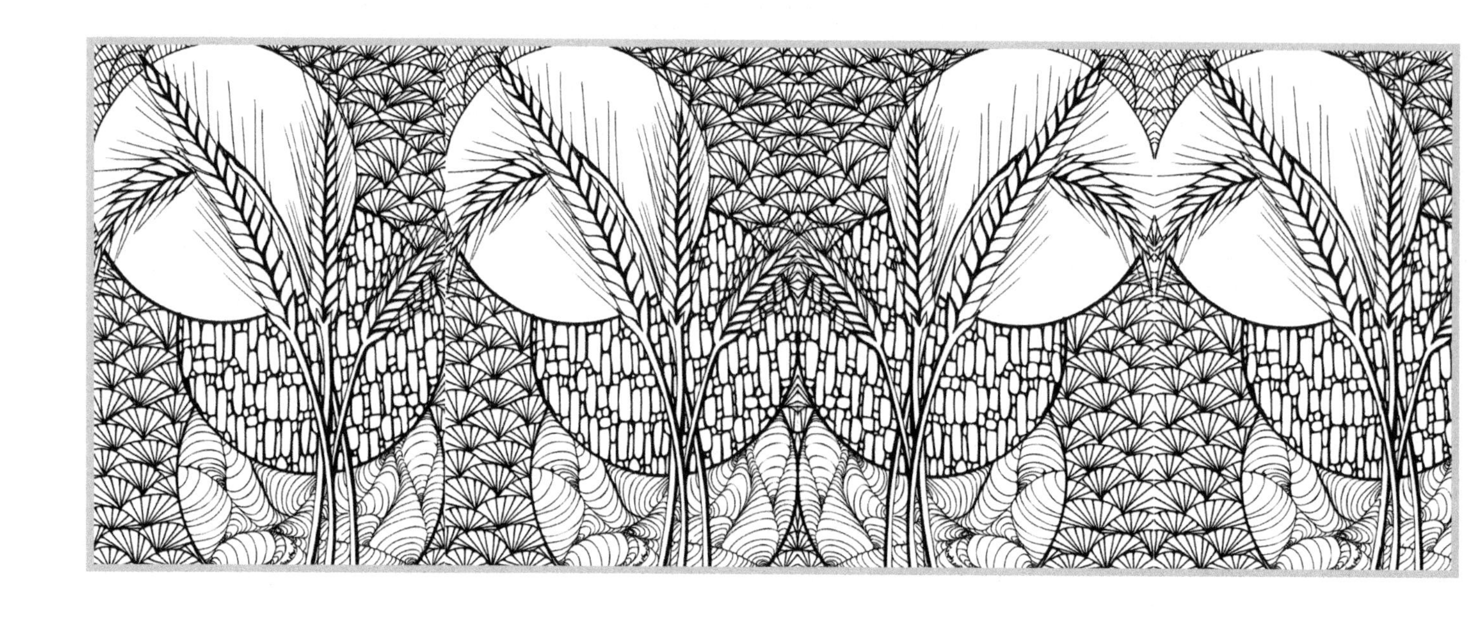

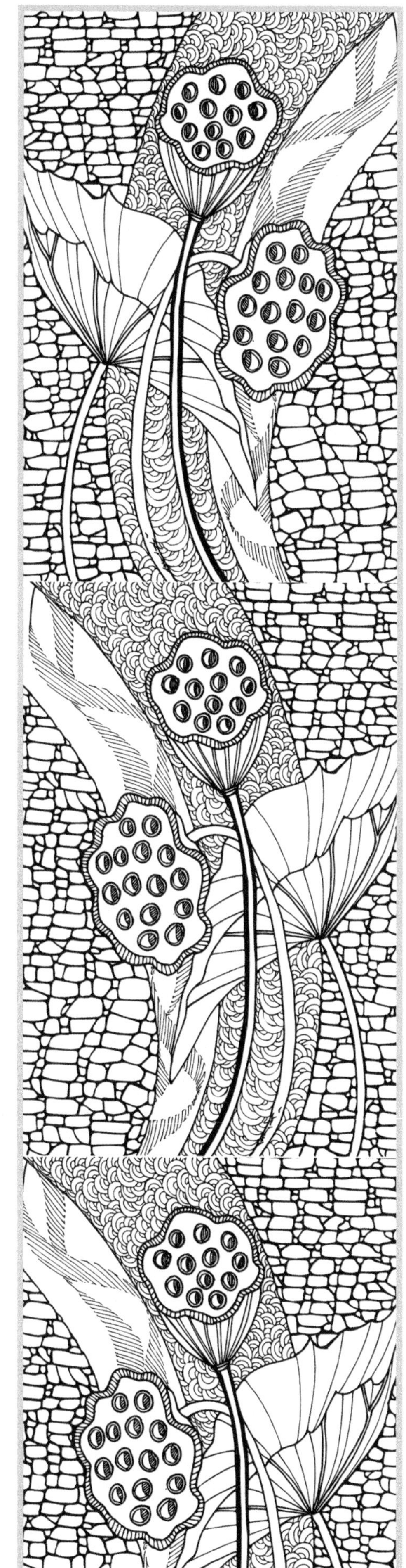

The Sower

"The sower sows the word."
Mark 4:14

In the parable of the sower Jesus made a startling declaration. He called God's Word "seed." He did not say it was "like" seed.

Pause and think about that.

Every characteristic demonstrated by seeds was also a characteristic of His Word! If we grasp the power of the seed, we will then understand the power of His Word.

Without modern photography, which magnified the crisp symmetry and elegance of seeds, I would have remained oblivious to their beauty. To a casual observer, their apparent plainness would never merit a closer look, nor inspire the drawings in this journal. Seeds are so varied and gorgeous that I could happily fill many books with drawings of them before exhausting my enthusiasm. However, their power and potential as the metaphor Jesus used inspires me far more than their visual charm.

Seeds are seemingly unremarkable. They are abundantly available and possess tremendous power to produce life. Yet they lie dormant unless provided with optimum conditions for growth. God's Word is no different.

Words overwhelm us. They scream at us in enormous type from billboards, ping on electronic devices, and vie continually for our attention. Although their visual assault is loud, it pales in comparison to the auditory bombardment that plagues our waking moments. Everyone has an opinion, is full of words, and is an expert.

Words are addicting; we feel a compulsion to cast them about, from the toddler just learning the power of "no" to the talk-show host tearing someone to shreds with caustic vocabulary. They flow so continually that I am certain there is not a moment when someone somewhere on this planet is not speaking.

In stark contrast, there are God's words in the Bible. They hardly make their presence known. His Word (which we will consider as a cohesive whole) does not shout at you, force you, or overwhelm you. The TV remote will grab your attention more readily than a Bible gathering dust somewhere.

Other than the few occasions when spoken by someone, His words remain silent in books or electronic devices, dormant until read, believed, and acted upon. Over the centuries, many have attempted to wipe them out. Yet they have endured, strangely protected on sacred pages, waiting to be discovered and contemplated—and yes, carefully sown.

It is just as easy to carelessly read God's Word without ever absorbing its beauty or experiencing its power as it is to trample upon a seed, never witnessing the mighty tree it could one day become!

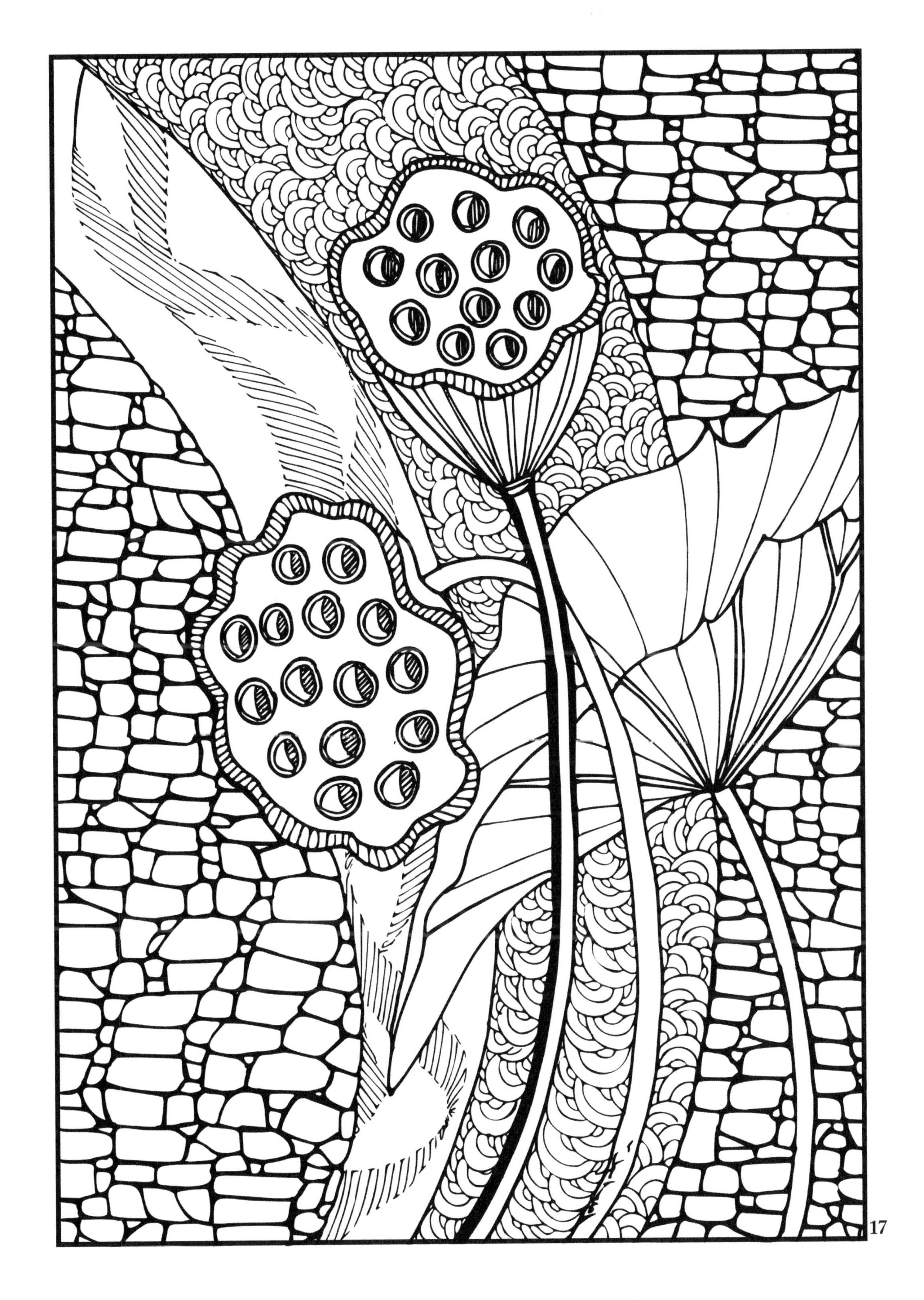

Sacred Seed

If God's Word is seed, as Jesus taught, then it possesses a dynamic power that is unseen to the casual observer. It merits reverence, awe, and careful handling as we would treat great treasure.

In cathedrals, we reverently pause under soaring ceilings in the jeweled hush of light streaming from stained glass windows. Our thoughts are lifted higher as we contemplate the grandeur of God. How far removed from us in character and power is He, as are the highest reaches of the sanctuary! There, under nave and arch, we sense the holiness of God.

Yet seated in the pew below we hold lightly the Bible, which are His thoughts imprinted crisply on translucent paper. His promises, admonitions, and instructions possess the power to change our lives. It's easy to be casual about the Bible; the same letters of the alphabet that make up our language also form God's Word. There are no sacred, magical characters of script that shimmer and hint of their supernatural power. Like the microscopic seed, the Word's appearance at a cursory glance is unremarkable, even downright ordinary.

The seed that drifted about in the wind remained unnoticed until magnified by the lens of a skilled photographer. Only then did the beauty of its form become captivating. Yet there was still no telling of its potential to become a mighty, fruit-bearing tree, yielding bushel upon bushel of nourishment year after year!

God's Word is the same, yielding its riches only upon a closer, more reverential look. Its power will remain untapped unless believed and acted upon in the quiet passage of time. Therefore a deeper study is definitely time well spent.

Write out your commitment to treasure the sacredness of His Word. Purpose to always treat it as holy, whether you are reading it yourself or listening to someone else. Some congregations rise at the reading of the Word. What a beautiful way to demonstrate its sanctity! Instill that holy pause in some meaningful way in your own actions every time you pick up your Bible to read. That reverent action will translate into greater faith in the words you read within.

The next few pages are for you to journal the promises that God speaks to your heart as you spend time in His Word. Cherish them as holy, sacred, and powerful. Describe what they mean to you at this moment in time, and add to it as God reveals more.

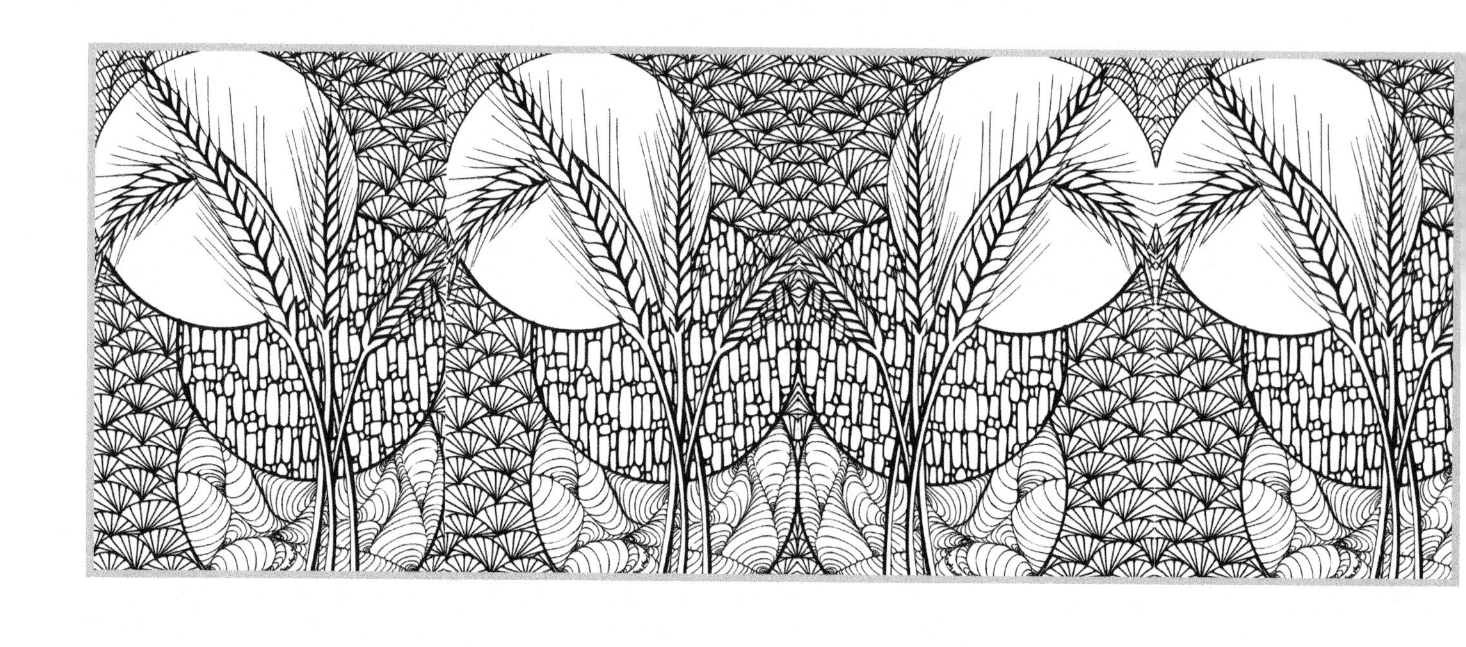

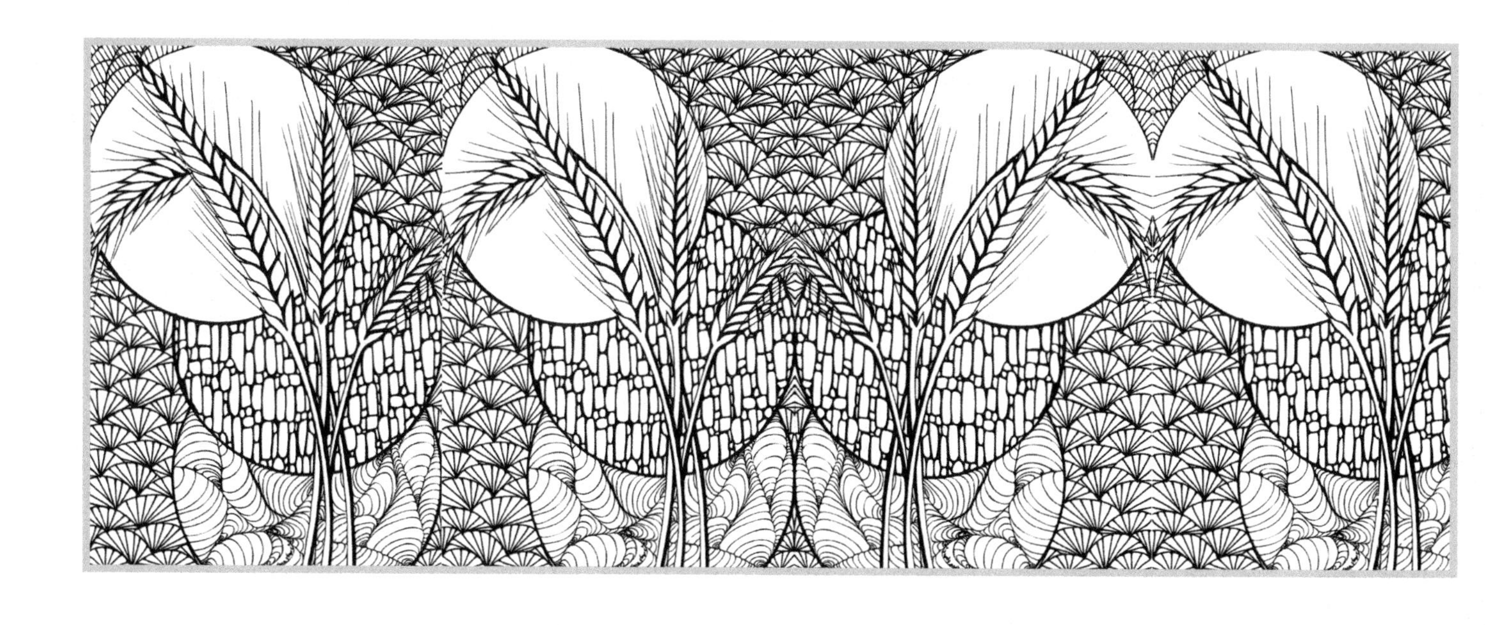

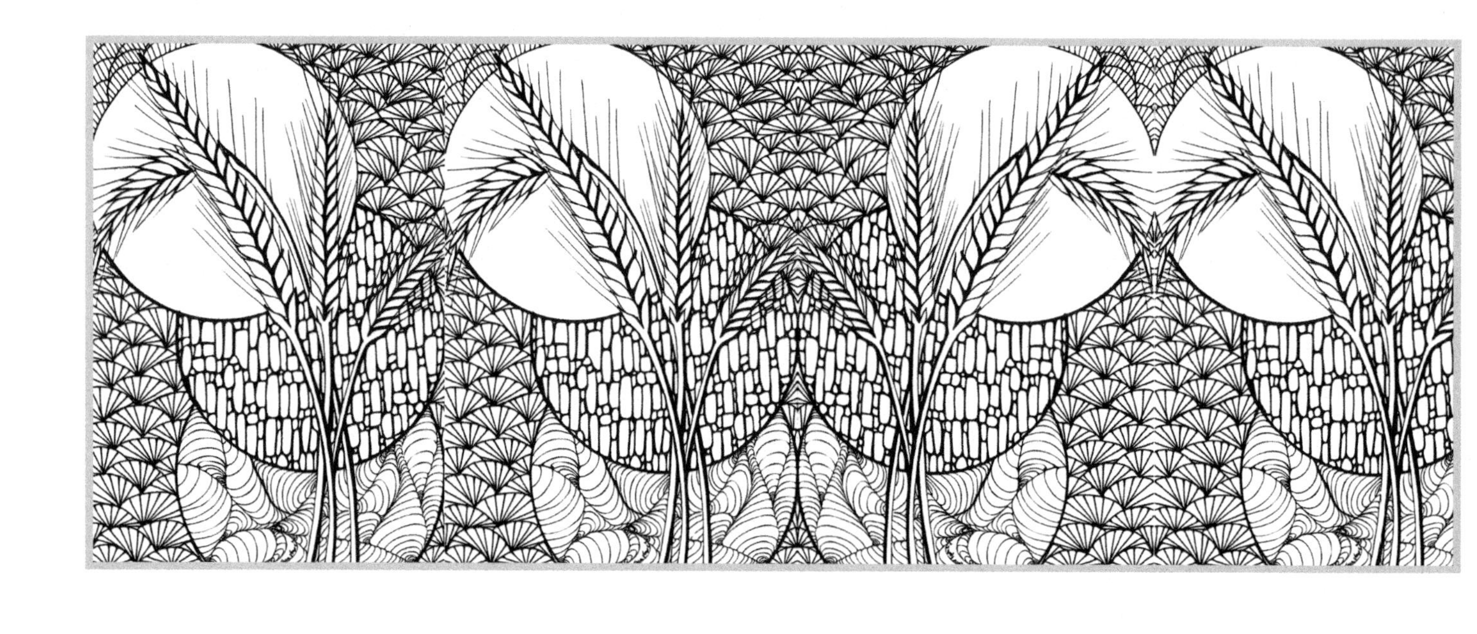

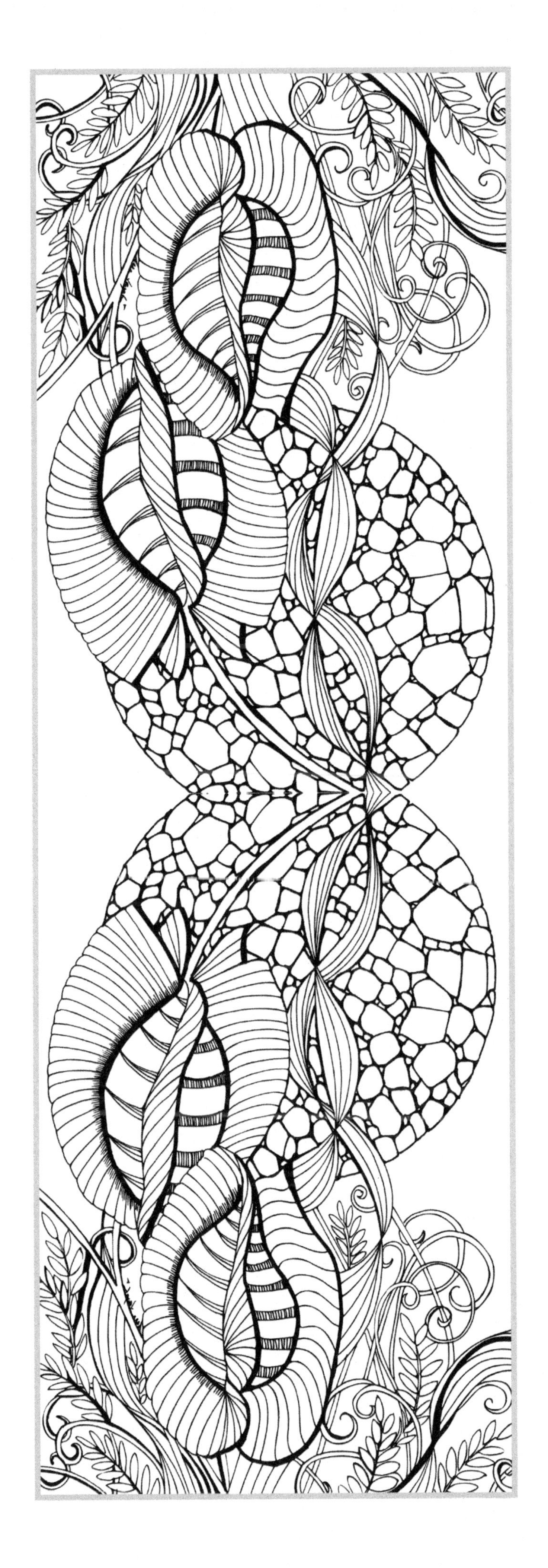

The Silver Screen

Cops were killed as they bravely served
Some said, "They got what they deserved"
I clicked to watch protesters scream
Spewing hate in a bilious stream

Switched the channel, someone cooked
Spilled empty words wherever I looked
Clicked at once to the sound of laughter
Jokes forgotten a moment after

With thoughts of food, I clicked once more
Heard a man speak as he paced the floor
"Will you trust God's boundless grace?"
Asked his raspy voice and sweating face

Be not quick to dismiss his kind
Or hastily deem his speech unrefined
"Love God," said he, "it's never too late"
Add faith to his words, they will germinate

Turn not away from this sower of words
If you long for a life as free as the birds
Look past his gestures and clammy face
That God's Word in your heart may find its place

Words of the Book from the glowing screen
By far more potent than what they seem
Need the soil of faith to multiply
It's God who sows them from on high

Seeds Reproduce

Once a year the sweetgum tree that casts its welcoming shade over my garage drops fat seeds by the dozens. They crunch crisply under my tires as I back out of the driveway. Squirrels scramble everywhere in a frenzy of activity, gathering what is spared. Comical, furry creatures of continual action, they struggle with a tough choice—gather these nuggets of nutrition in order to store them for later consumption in the middle of a bleak winter, or feast on them right away?

"Eat them quick!" I'd advise them, if they cared to listen. Their stored treasures are a nuisance to me, since they unfailingly sprout a season later in my flower beds or in the middle of the lawn, where I have no interest in growing another enormous tree.

That the seeds will reproduce, given the right conditions, is indisputable. Therein lies their power.

Are you confident that the seed of every promise in the Bible will unfailingly manifest if you provide optimum conditions for its growth? That inner certainty is faith, which God deems more precious than gold.

Faith takes God at His Word even if at first there is no outward evidence of change manifested. Faith trusts Him for a harvest when all you have are a handful of minuscule seeds that look insignificant. Faith is substance that God finds invaluable. Faith in His Word will produce a life like no other—a life worth living.

"Now faith is the substance of things hoped for, the evidence of things not seen."
Hebrews 11:1

The Perfection of Purpose

I used to wonder why God never bothers to defend Himself. He is often maligned and misunderstood; evil is attributed to Him when good is what He promises. How often I've watched people shake their fists and rail at Him when things didn't go as planned. Surely it must grieve Him, who is only good! Yet He remains silent.

Perhaps it is because His purposes ultimately prevail. Why should He defend perfection? We are the ones who miss out on His benefits if we refuse to cooperate.

His plans for us are outlined in the Bible in great detail. With infinite patience, the Holy Spirit will help us understand their every nuance. We are still left with the responsibility of studying, understanding, believing, and then working in harmony with them. Only then do we deliberately place our lives in the blessed path of God's unfailing purposes.

"So will My word be which goes forth from My mouth;
it will not return to Me empty."
Isaiah 55:11

The Blessed Unknown

He planned for time when time was not
More lofty than our highest thought
God spoke of it in but a whisper
Words in ink on gossamer paper

Yet unknown is their certain might
Like seeds in soil tucked out of sight
In hearts they must be hidden well
For a harvest only time will tell

So treat each word as treasure rare
Nurturing it with faith and care
God shall accomplish all He wills
His words to you He will fulfill

The Parable of the Sower

How I love the stories Jesus told! Read the parable of the sower as told by Jesus in Matthew 13 and Luke 8. We've heard it taught that the four soils represent four types of people with different responses to the gospel (the good news) of His kingdom. Some forget the words as soon as they hear, others scoff at it, and still others receive it for a season, only to fall away at the first challenge brought about by life's trying circumstances. Only one of those four actually produces a harvest of the seed that fell upon it. That is true.

As Christians, it's easy to quickly presume that our hearts are good soil, eager for the seed of God's Word. We expect the hundredfold harvest in every area of our lives. Why not? We are believers. Surely Jesus is referring to those who don't believe.

But perhaps we too may be guilty of receiving His Word at different times in our lives exactly as Jesus described it—with dull, stony, unkempt, or thorny hearts.

His Word is often difficult to grasp. We read it quickly and think we are full of faith, only to waver at the first hint of opposition. Who has not found themselves floundering in faith when life becomes overwhelming and troubles seem greater than His promises to us? We too are guilty! Our hearts are fickle, sometimes responsive and sometimes not. Let's ask Jesus for His help to keep from falling into the traps He described!

"My eyes are continually toward the Lord, for He will pluck my feet out of the net."

Psalm 25:15

May we be eager to be the good soil of hearts filled with integrity, submissive to God and His Word. By describing right and wrong responses to His Word, Jesus offers us hope. If we thoughtfully examine our lives, receive His correction, and document our challenges, we will learn from our weaknesses. By those actions we demonstrate our desire to please Him. Then we will surely become the soil that consistently produces the hundredfold harvest.

"Light is sown like seed for the righteous

And gladness for the upright in heart."

Psalm 97:11

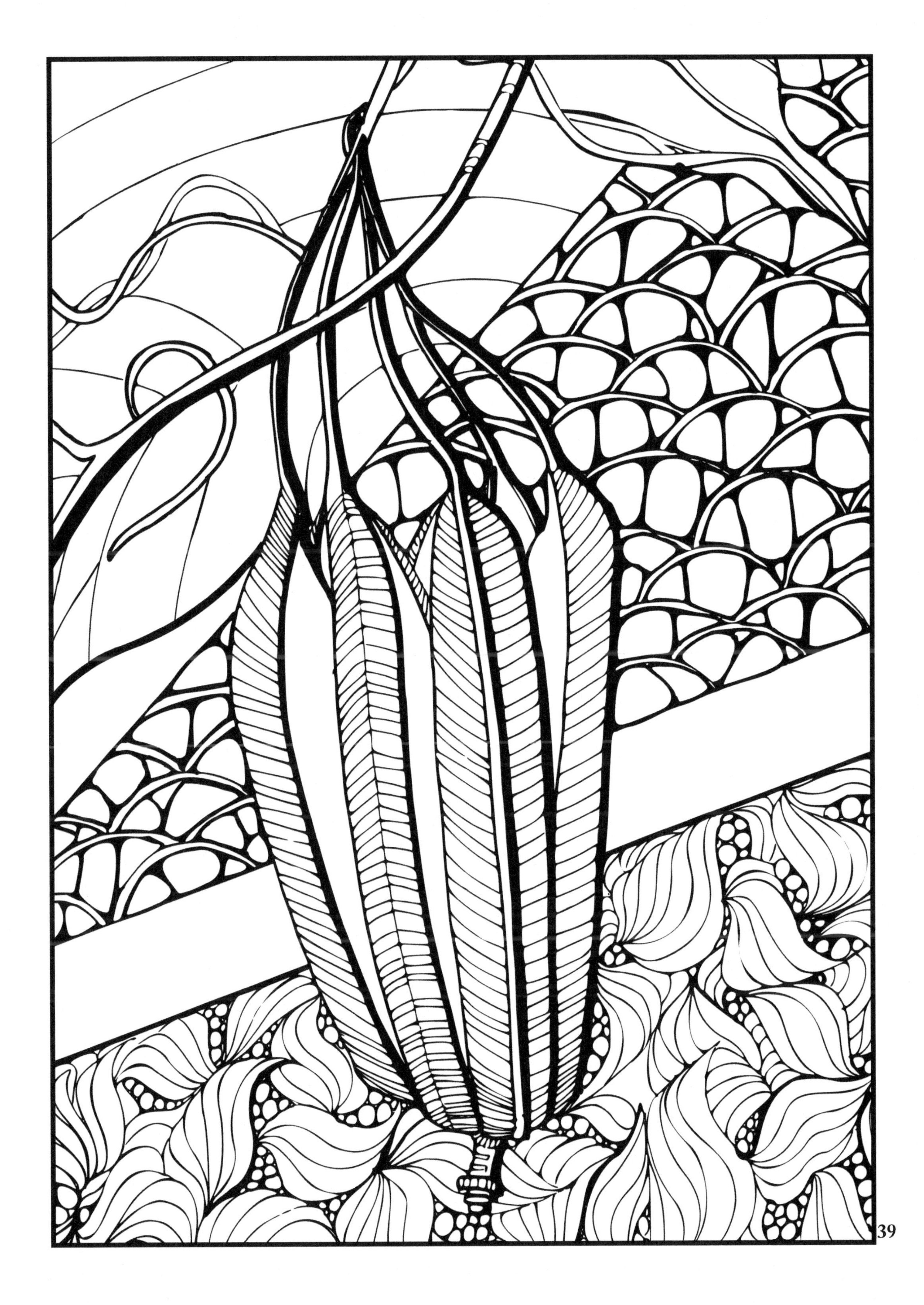

The Certain Harvest

Four types of soil, each somewhat different
Received much seed, dry, dull, and dormant
Kernels of power with secrets for gardens
Would they transform soil that lay barren?

Bruised the seed much flattened by feet
Crushing its life, 'twas a rapid defeat
No chance for blooms or fruitful orchards
When trampled upon or stolen by birds

Bouncing off rock, settling in crevices
Seeds lay naked to the passing breezes
Roots searched in vain to find safe anchor
In thimbles of soil grew only to wither

Brave grew a shoot from seed amidst thorns
Sought valiantly to weather the storms
Choked was its life and stifled its hope
Misshapen its fruit as for light it groped

But sweet was the soil, freshly tilled
Cleared of rubble with loam refilled
Thrived seeds there for seasons untold
To bear much fruit, even a hundredfold

"And when he sowed, some seeds fell by the way side, and the fowls came and devoured them up."
Matthew 13:4, King James Version

The Wayside

The King James Version of the verse above conveys a wonderful sense of immediacy. Can't you hear the flapping of wings and see the birds swooping down on the exposed seeds? As Jesus explained the metaphor, a lack of understanding of God's Word is the reason the enemy so quickly devours the seeds on the wayside.

You love God, as I do, and long to walk in His ways. Why else would you be working patiently in this journal? Yet despite our best intentions, we face a continual challenge to our faith. It is what we think we know. Our views, shaped by our own experiences, the stories of others, and lessons from childhood, form our understanding.

The Greek word *hodos,* used for "wayside," describes the common path: trampled upon, hard and unyielding. Hundreds have walked on it before, their footsteps stamping out a collective wisdom appropriately called "common sense," which unfortunately does not leave room for the supernatural work of God.

Every promise in the Bible paints a vision of a superb future and immediately presents us with a choice. Our minds cannot fathom how it could come to pass in our limited, muddled lives. "What you are experiencing now," whispers the bland voice of common sense, "is how things always happen. Why should it be any different this time?" On the other hand, faith reminds us that God, who made the promise, will grant us the outcome we are unable to envision. The choice of how to respond is left up to us.

"Common sense" forms the dust of the wayside path. Entertaining it by dwelling on it permits the precious seed of God's promise to be quickly devoured by the birds. I'm guilty of having done this so often; I've calculated how things were likely to happen based on how they happened in the past to me, or to someone else, and then resigned myself to that sad outcome.

It doesn't have to be that way!

Don't let the promises God whispers to your heart be trampled upon or stolen by the birds. If you've done it before, don't despair. We've all too often trod that dusty road in vain. Jesus warned us so that we can avoid that deadly pitfall.

When God sows His promise in my heart, I purpose to keep it far from the wayside path, which is common and unremarkable, possessing no power to bring about the abundant life He guarantees. You can do the same.

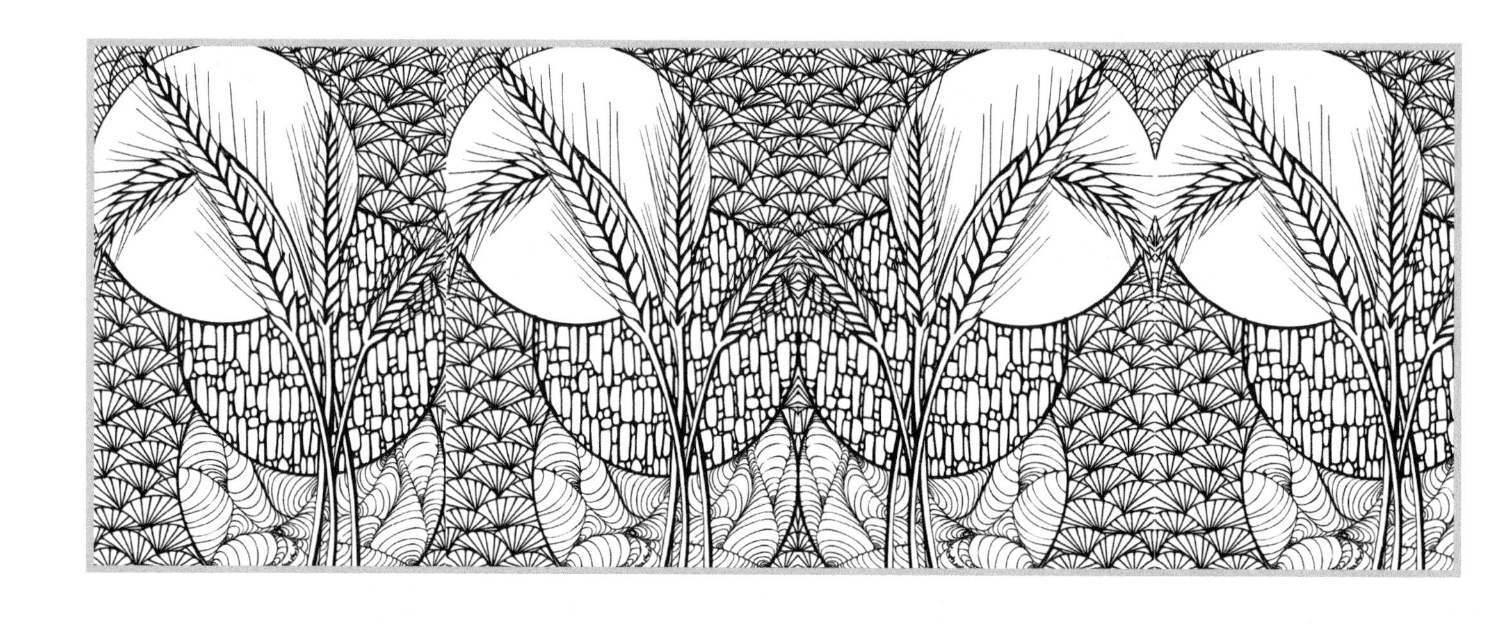

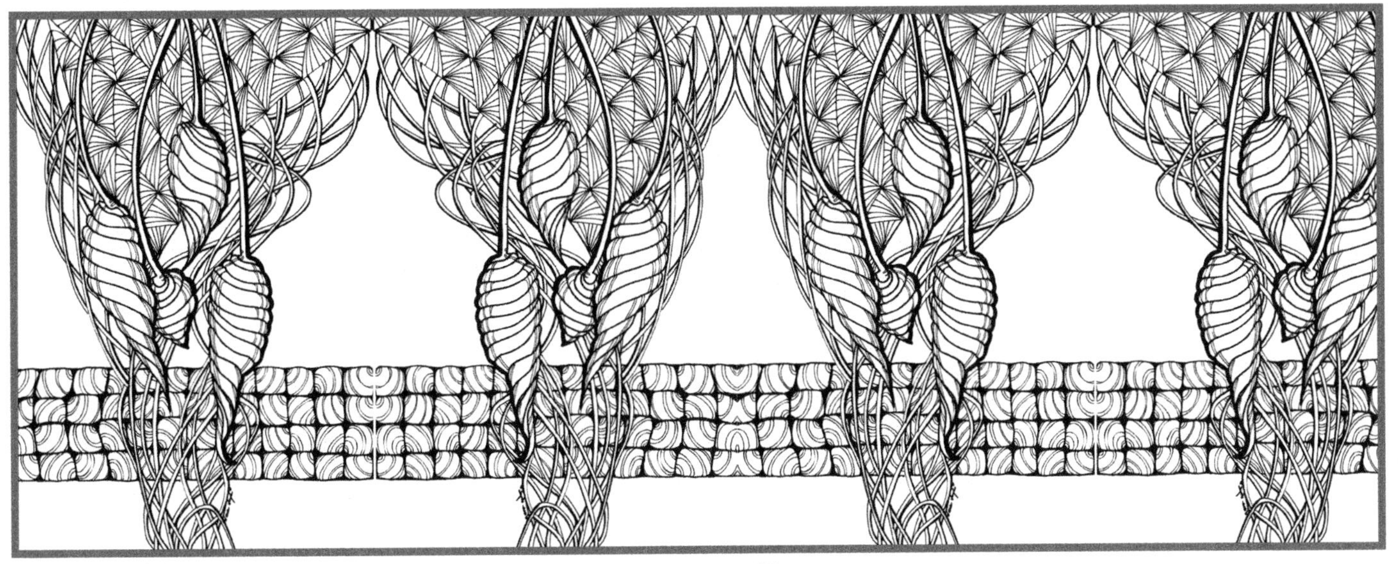

Joy on the Rocks

"Other seed fell on rocky soil, and as soon as it grew up,

it withered away, because it had no moisture."

Luke 8:6

I've often listened to a testimony of God's faithfulness and been greatly encouraged. My heart raced at possibilities for my own life. The Holy Spirit would gently remind me that God does not play favorites. If He worked this way in someone else's life, He would surely work in mine! So with joy, I too entertained the hope that the same promise could be mine. I've floated out of church, excited and full of happy expectation. You've probably felt the same.

Then the heat of battle began. The sun rose in the midday sky and beat down upon my little shoot of faith. Not bothering to commit the promise to memory or ask if there was more I ought to do to nurture it, I lived life oblivious to the certainty that the Word would be contested. My shoot of faith began to dry out. I was too busy to replenish the lost moisture, so its shallow roots shriveled and the hope I once entertained withered completely and died. Sadly, I even forgot that I was once excited at just that very promise. The next time I heard it, all I remembered was my lack of results, and that precious seed lost its power to produce.

Rocky ground, although hard and nonporous, still has pockets of space where good soil settles in and seeds can root. Yet it resists the softening of water, except in those little crevices where fertile soil can make a temporary home. The heat of the day can be unrelenting, drying out whatever weak shoot briefly rooted there. Isn't it far better to prepare your heart by diligently removing all rocks to leave only loose, fertile soil that can easily be softened by water?

"Those on the rocky soil are those who, when they hear, receive the word with joy;

and these have no firm root; they believe for a while, and in time of temptation fall away."

Luke 8:13

When have you done the same? Ask Jesus to show you when you received His Word gladly and then quit believing its marvelous promise. Where did the hardness of heart creep in? Express your insight on the next few pages. Then as you color the next seed, replant that specific promise deliberately by being tender and yielded, trusting God to finish what He has spoken.

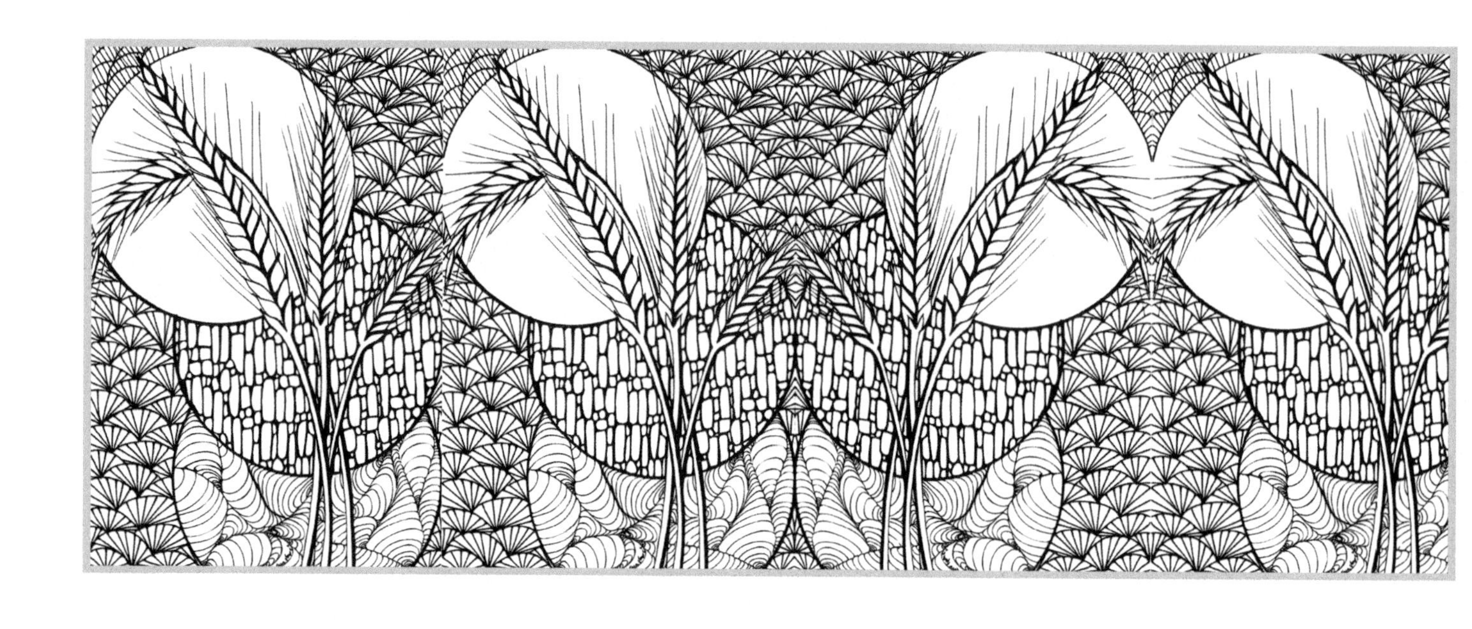

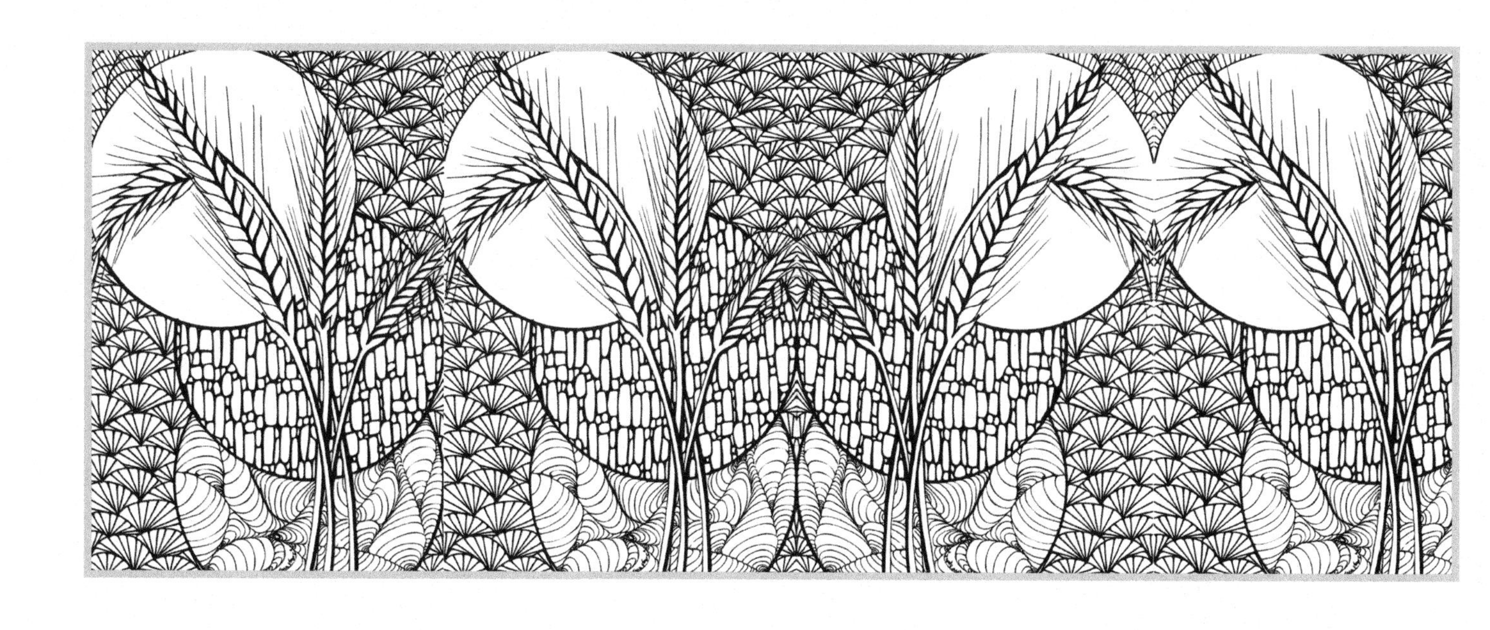

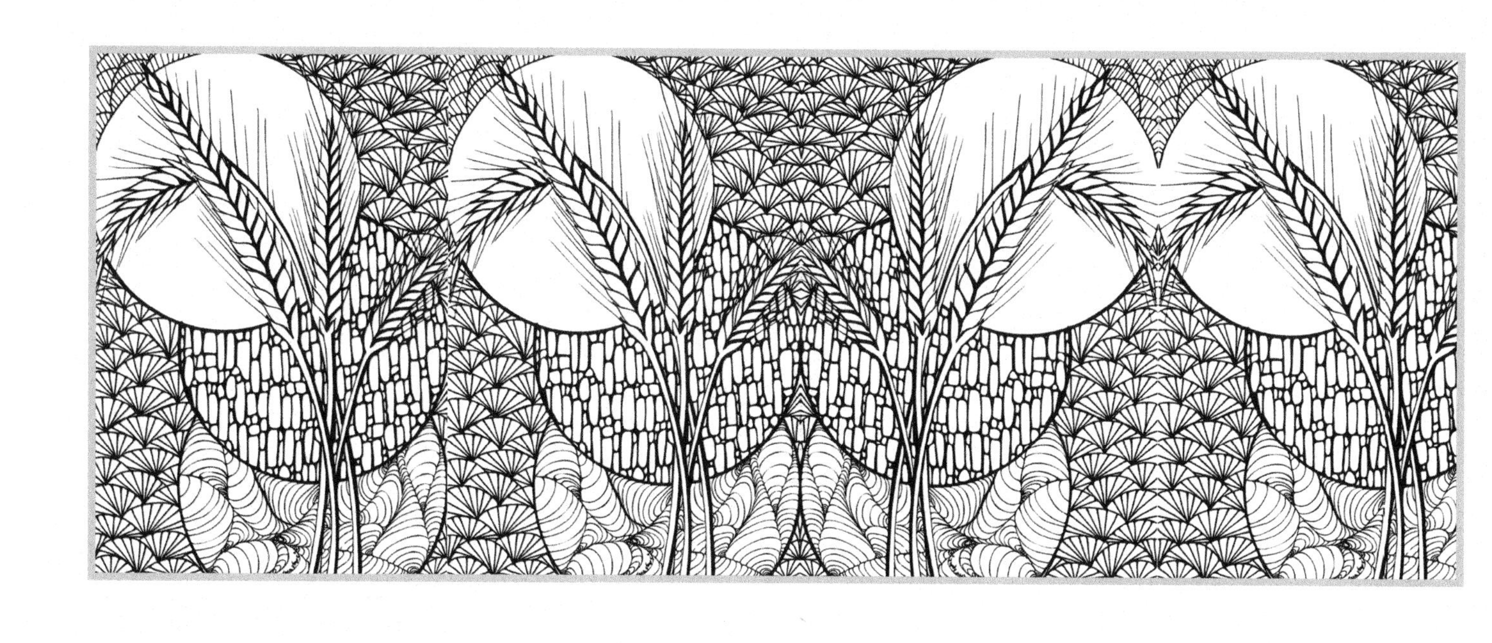

Seed Among Thorns

"And that which fell among thorns are they,
which, when they have heard,
go forth,
and are choked with cares and riches
and pleasures of this life,
and bring no fruit to perfection."
Luke 8:14, King James Version

Thorny ground is unpleasant and has few redeeming qualities. Seeds that fell on thorny ground still saw the sun, felt some rain, and sprouted. Tender shoots snaked up and away from arid ground. They unfurled a hesitant leaf or two, only to be pierced by the thorns, producing worthless fruit.

Have you read a promise from God, believed as you read it, and then continued on your way without giving it much further thought? Nothing changed in your thoughts or actions. That was seed that fell among thorns.

A closer look at the translation of the Greek word *poreuō,* used for *"go forth"* is interesting. The Blue Letter Bible says that it means "to pursue the journey on which one has entered or to continue on one's journey."

We are each on a journey, and much of it is of our own making. Our plans fill our minds—things we must do, things we'd like to do, and things we ought to do. When interrupted with precious words from the Bible, we are faced with a choice. Do we cherish them, act on them, nurture them, and expect good from them? Or do we gloss over them and continue on our journey? If we choose the latter, those words became seeds that fell among the thorns.

They may sprout and grow a little, but they will eventually be smothered by thorns, choking their life and resulting in misshapen fruit.

None of us wants that! Yet when we are casual about God's Word, it is like neglecting to clear the ground of thorns before planting.

Uproot Worry; Ignore Distractions!

Cares, riches, and pleasures of this life prevent the formation of beautiful fruit. That was the fate of the seed that fell on thorny ground. Who could imagine that worry would be just as troublesome as the distractions of riches and pleasures! Yet Jesus stated it was just as deadly.

Spend some time clearing your thorny weeds away. Fear and faith cannot coexist, just as worry and peace cannot. What worry has kept you from nurturing the precious promises of God?

"Be anxious for nothing, but in everything by prayer and supplication with thanksgiving let your requests be made known to God." Philippians 4:6

Please don't make the mistake of thinking that God does not want you to enjoy riches or live a pleasurable life. He does! But it must be received from Him and lived by faith to be truly satisfying and fruitful.

God is concerned with the affairs of our heart. Where do our affections lie—with Him or with the pursuit of material wealth without Him, which is a lifelong source of temptation?

"Instruct those who are rich in this present world not to be conceited or to fix their hope on the uncertainty of riches, but on God, who richly supplies us with all things to enjoy." 1 Timothy 6:17

God richly supplies us with all things. So why do we strive so much and enjoy so little? More thorns to remove—these caused by a misunderstanding of God's goodness and desire to bless us with abundance! To remedy that, write down Deuteronomy 28:1-14 in the next pages and sow it carefully in the good soil of your heart so that you never again doubt God's wonderful intentions toward you.

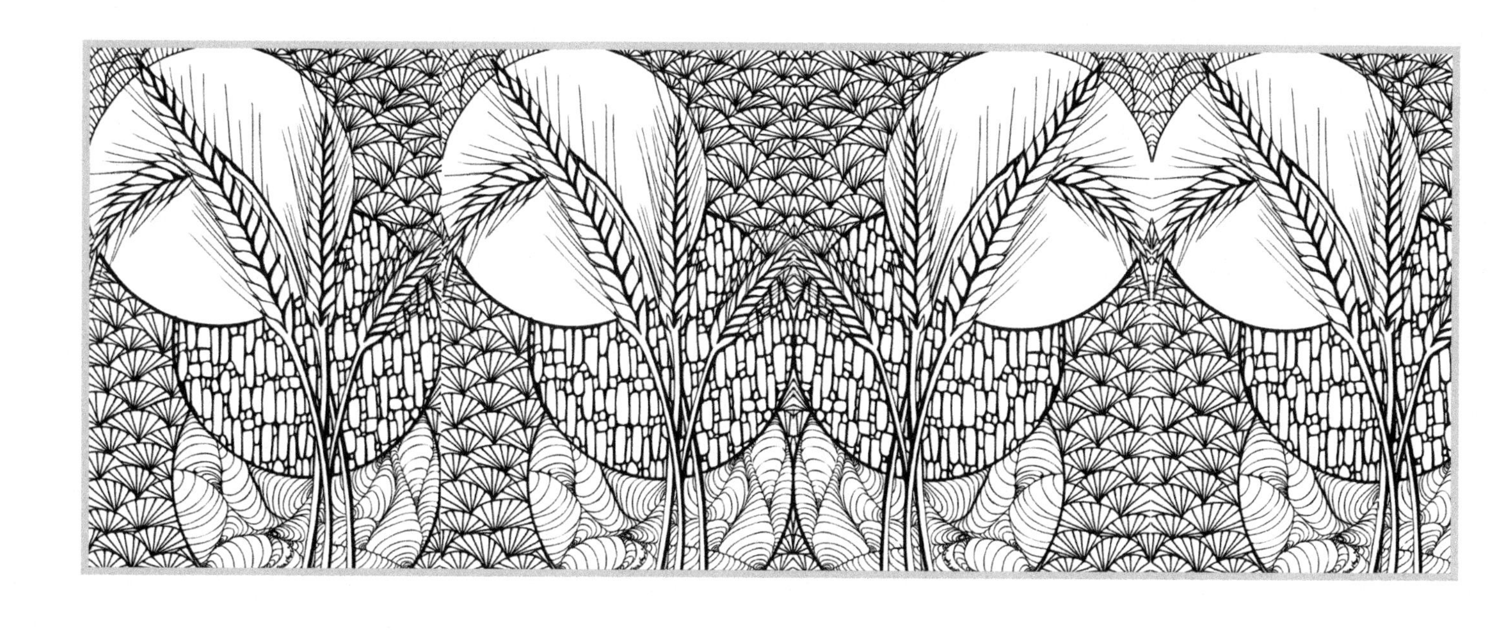

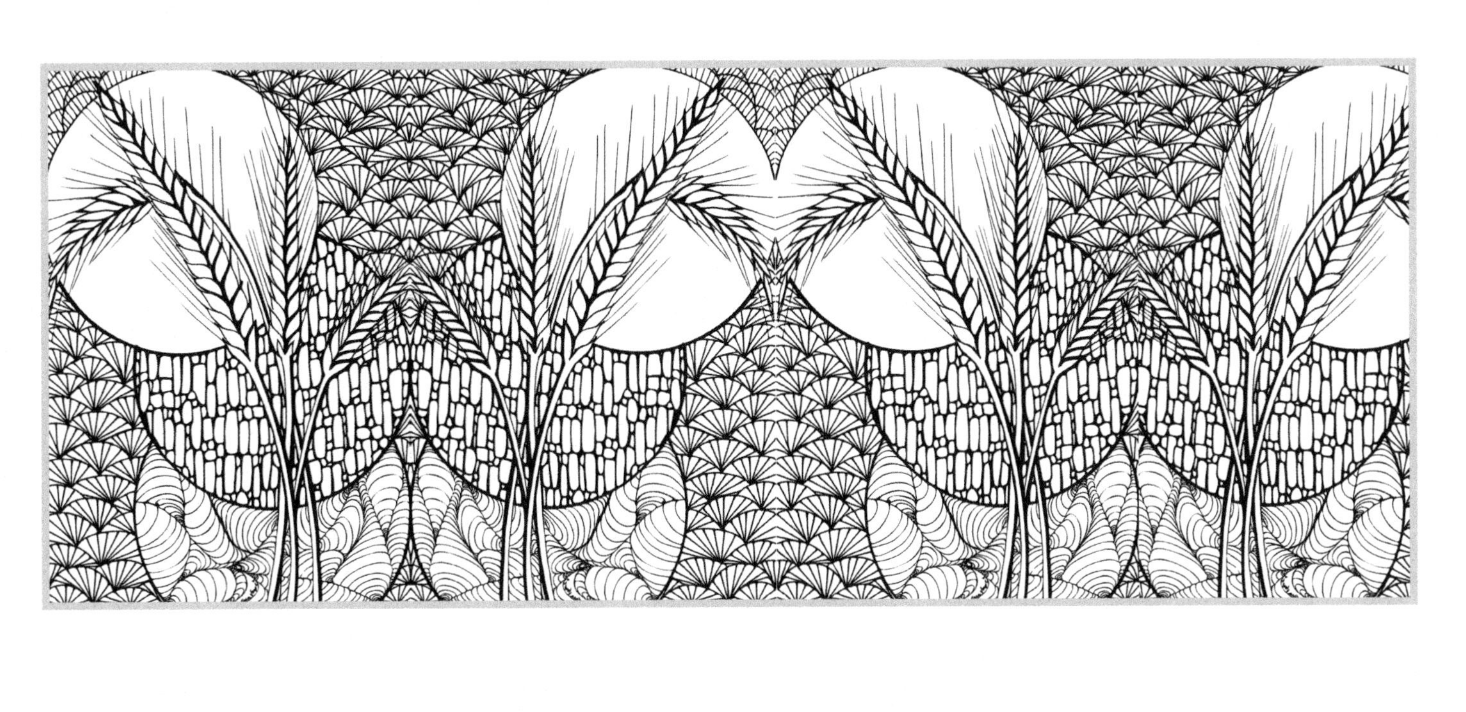

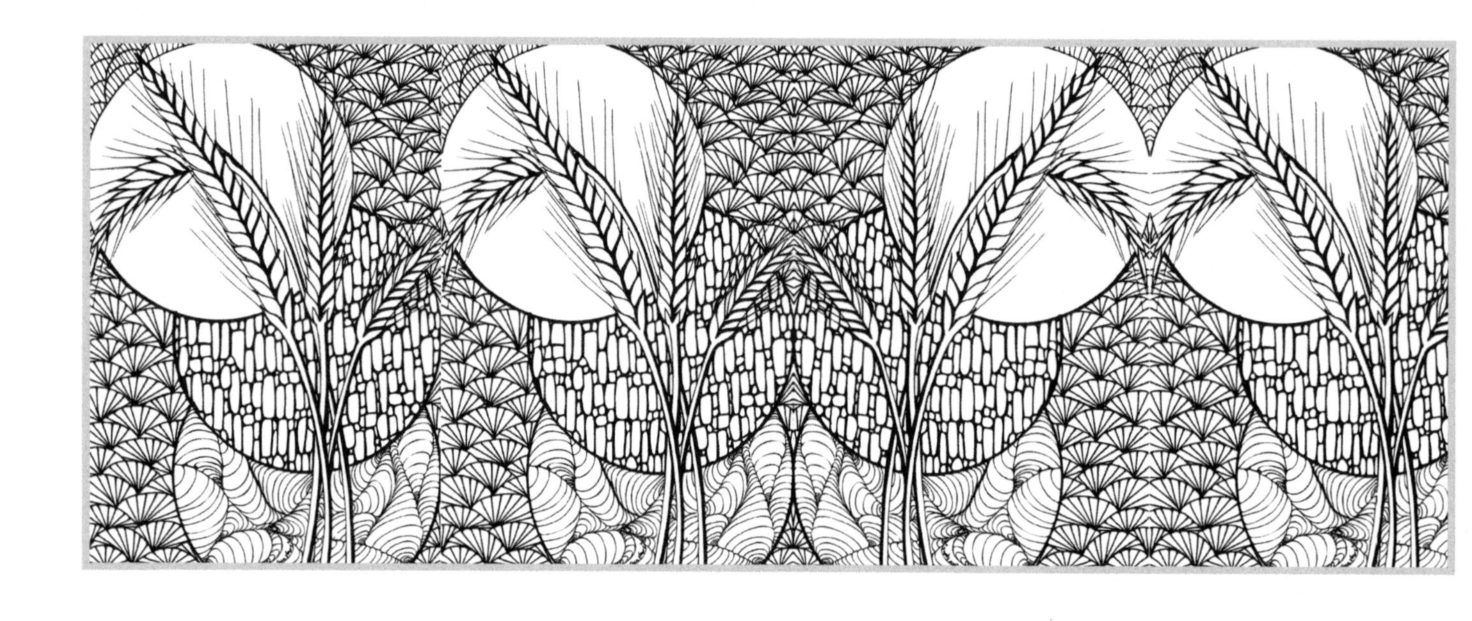

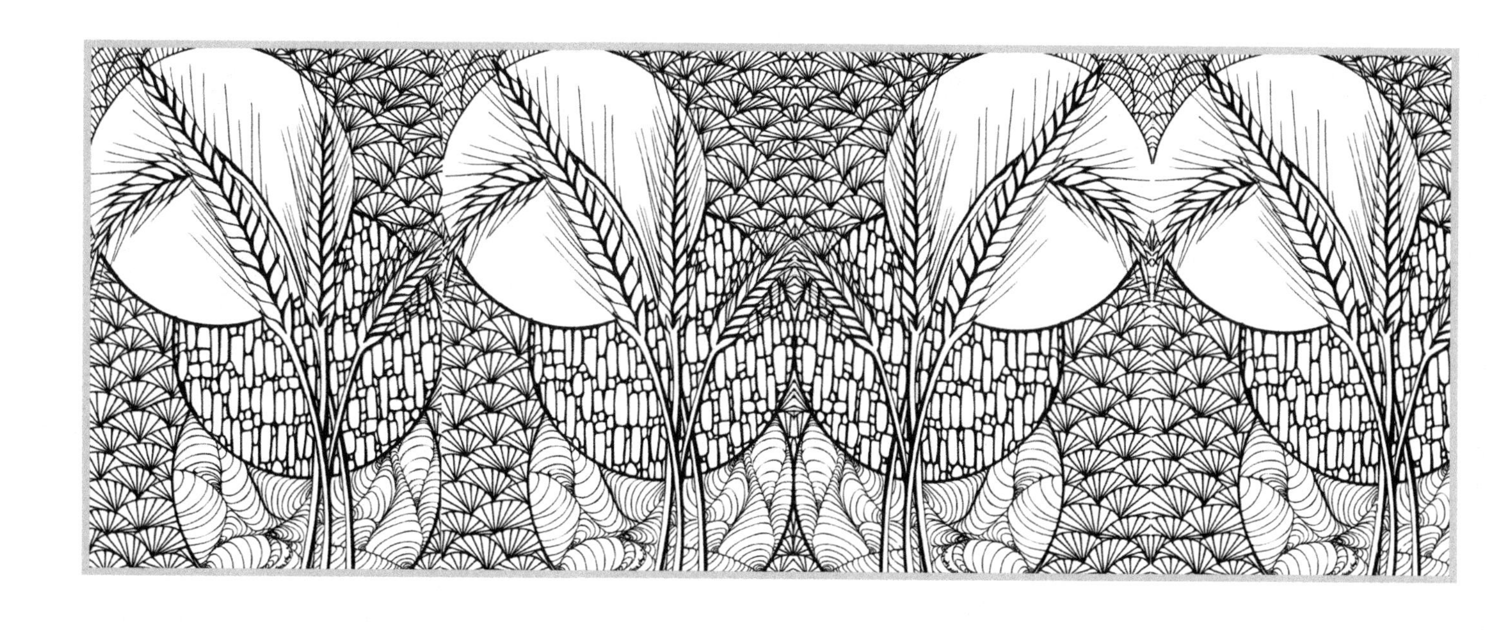

The Honest and Good Heart

***"But the seed in the good soil, these are the ones who have heard the word in an honest and good heart."* Luke 8:15**

Good soil is priceless; its value cannot be overestimated. Of the four soils Jesus described, this is the only one that produces a worthy harvest when seed is cast upon it. Will you expend the necessary energy to prepare soil that is ripe for a bountiful harvest?

Everything worth possessing is worth pursuing. Jesus equated fruitful soil with an "honest and good" heart that eagerly received His Word. Are you transparent before God? Examine your soil closely. See a rock? Out it goes. Pricked by thorny branches of worry, strife, or covetousness? Ouch! Get rid of them. Quick, pull those unsightly weeds! What are those? Lies masquerading as excuses, laziness, a bland faith, pride? Toss them in the rubbish heap! You're demonstrating your active commitment to purity.

Christians who enjoy close fellowship with Jesus are those who submit themselves to continual correction and change. Do you yield to a reprimand, or do you chafe when God speaks a word of correction into your life? Receiving corrective counsel with grace is an unfailing litmus test of a victorious, abundant life. Correction is never comfortable, but it can certainly be stomached if we keep the vision of a plentiful harvest before us.

Correction does not always need to be drastic. Sometimes it can be a gentle call back to trust.

In a challenging season in my life, I struggled to trust God. My son, who was then only five, wrapped his little arms around me and sang a popular song, which he had heard often on the radio.

"Peace be still," he sang, "the Father loves you. Peace, be still; the Father cares."

As his sweet voice sang, I had a choice to make—would I heed or disregard the voice of the Holy Spirit urging me back to faith simply because it came from the mouth of a child? Fortunately, the beauty of the moment reached through my darkness and touched me. God cared enough about me to use my little boy to redirect me to His path! It reminded me that my journey with Him is a walk of faith and not sight.

A command leaps off the pages of the Bible. How do you handle it? Correction could come from words spoken in a sermon, the counsel of a friend, or a glimpse into the life of another that demonstrates the importance of obedience. Will you stand corrected, or will you justify error? It is challenging to receive correction and to purpose to change. If you do, your heart becomes the sweet loam that receives the seed of His Word, which will certainly produce a worthwhile harvest.

Read 2 Timothy 3:16, Daniel 10:12, Revelation 3:19, and Proverbs 3:11. Use the next pages to write down those quiet nudges of the Holy Spirit urging you toward changes He is encouraging you to make in your life.

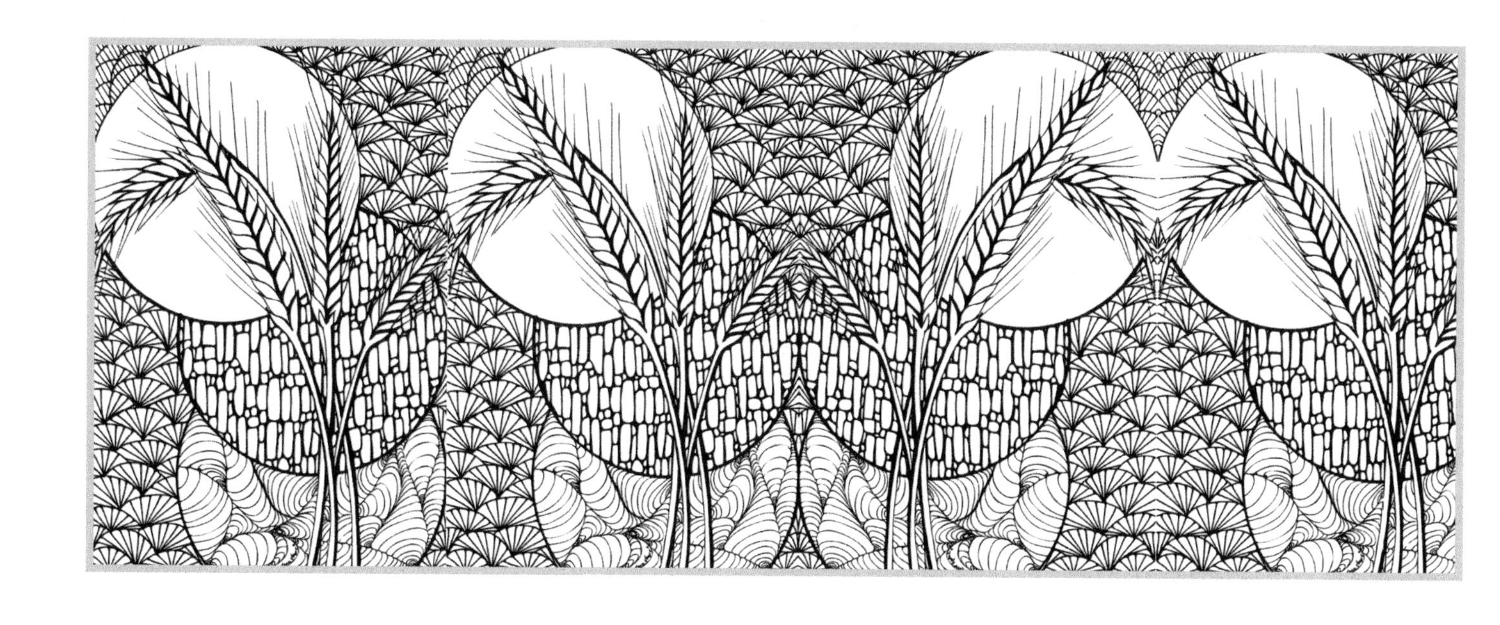

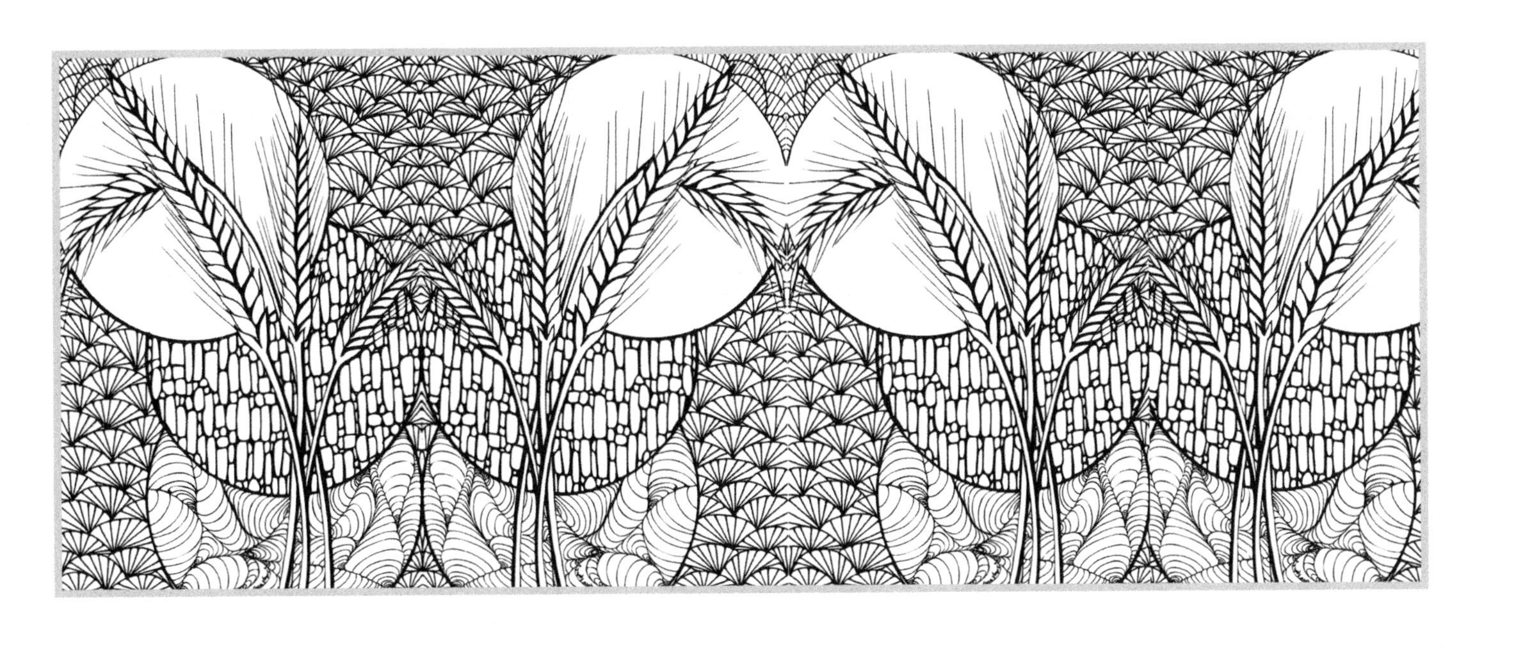

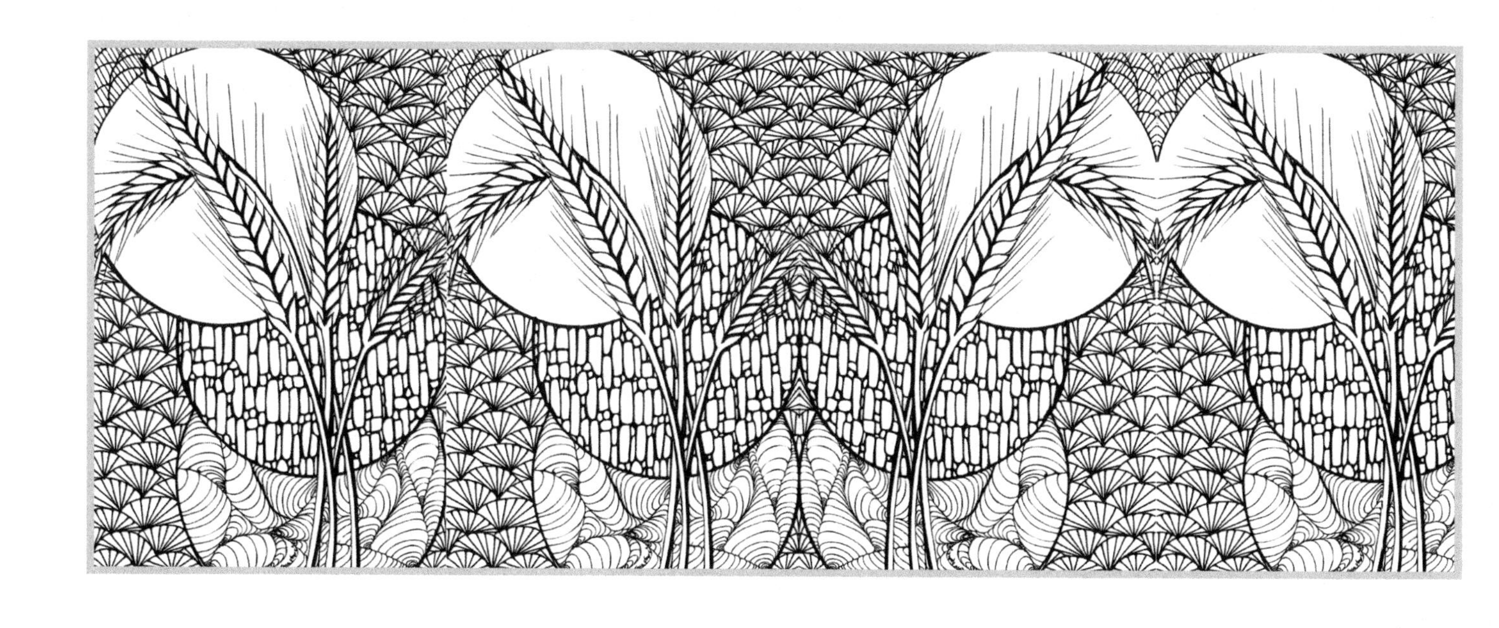

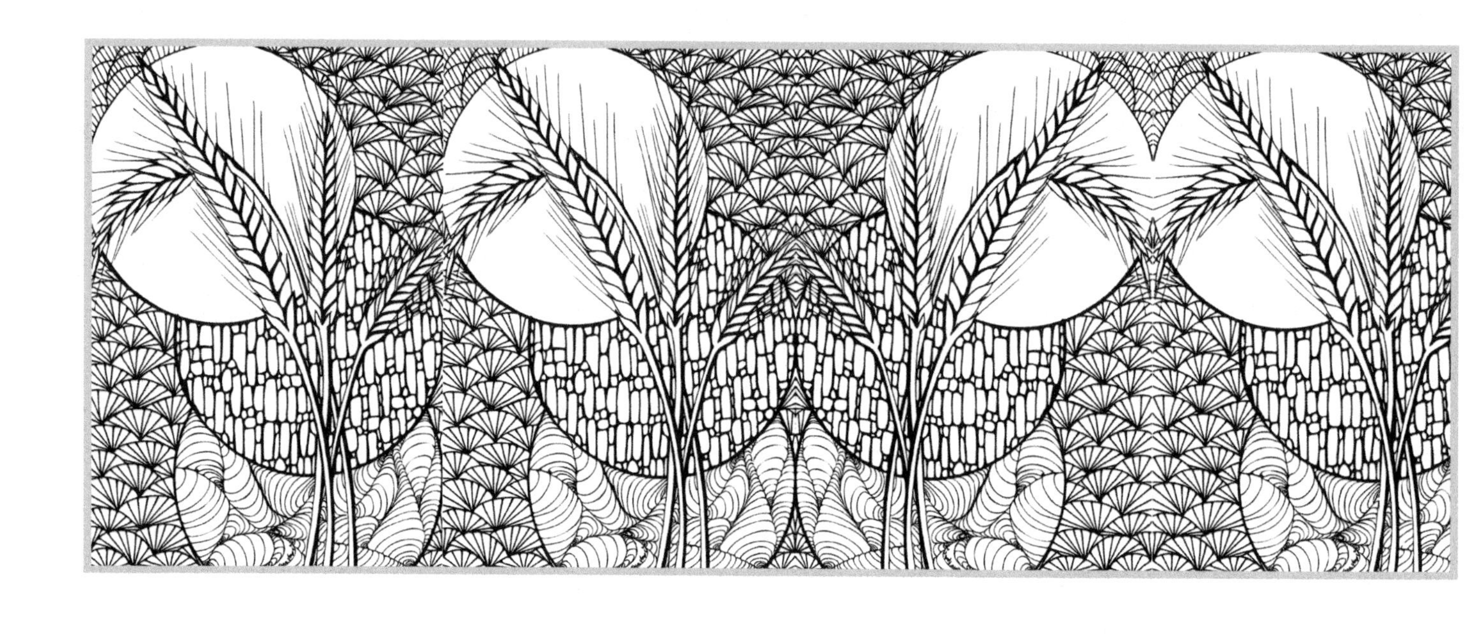

Fruit with Patience

***"...having heard the word, keep it, and bring forth fruit with patience."* Luke 8:15**

Keeping the Word is such an intriguing concept; it can make the difference between a bountiful harvest and no fruit at all. Maintaining faith in a promise of God takes deliberate action. The seed must be watered with faith until it germinates. When it eventually sprouts, watchfulness is required so that nothing harms the little sapling.

From the first planting of the seed until the formation of fruit, there is the painfully slow passage of time. Even when finally visible, fruit must slowly ripen before it is ready to harvest.

No one in their right mind would unearth a delicate sapling to see if it was forming roots. Visible evidence is unnecessary when we trust the process. If leaves are shooting up, then roots are matting the soil below even if unseen. Cooling our heels and being patient is part of the process, though I'll readily admit it is never easy!

When I see no immediate evidence of what God has promised coming to pass, I'm ashamed to admit I dismiss the promise, only to pick it back up in desperation, knowing well that without it I am without hope! I nurture the Word for a while and then despair that it may never come to pass. I waffle back and forth. That, I've learned, is the equivalent of jerking my shoot out of the ground, tossing it aside, and then trying to retrieve it a couple of days later to replant it! It stands little hope of becoming a mighty fruit-bearing tree.

Just reminding myself that fruit bearing is a long process requiring patience is half the battle won. Fortunately, patience is a fruit of the Spirit—a spiritual force with immense power. When we lean on the Lord, the Holy Spirit will work it in our lives until we see the fulfillment of that promise on which our hearts have pinned their hope.

Lord, may we be willing to stay the course until we see Your many precious promises come to pass in our lives!

Write in these next pages where you are in your journey with a specific promise. Are you in the planting, weeding, watering, or harvesting stage? Or are you patiently waiting for germination? Wherever you are in your journey, document it here. One day it will be wonderful to go back and see your progress!

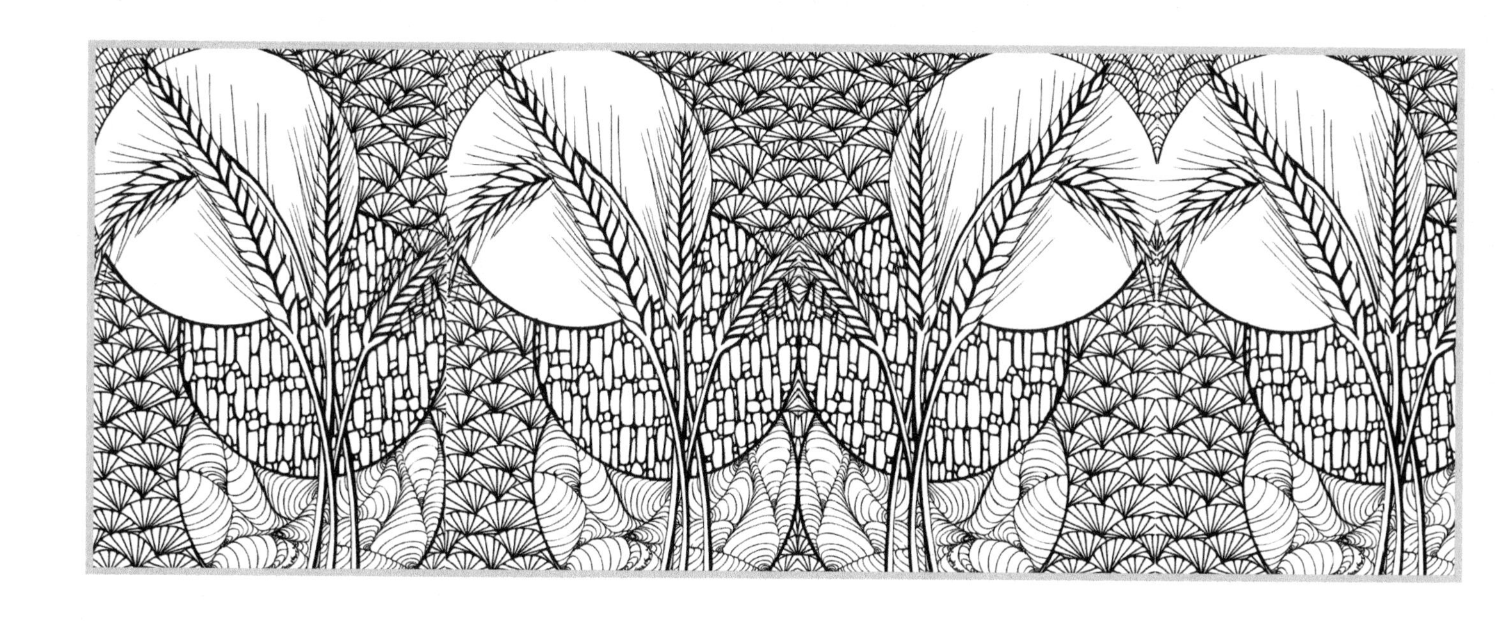

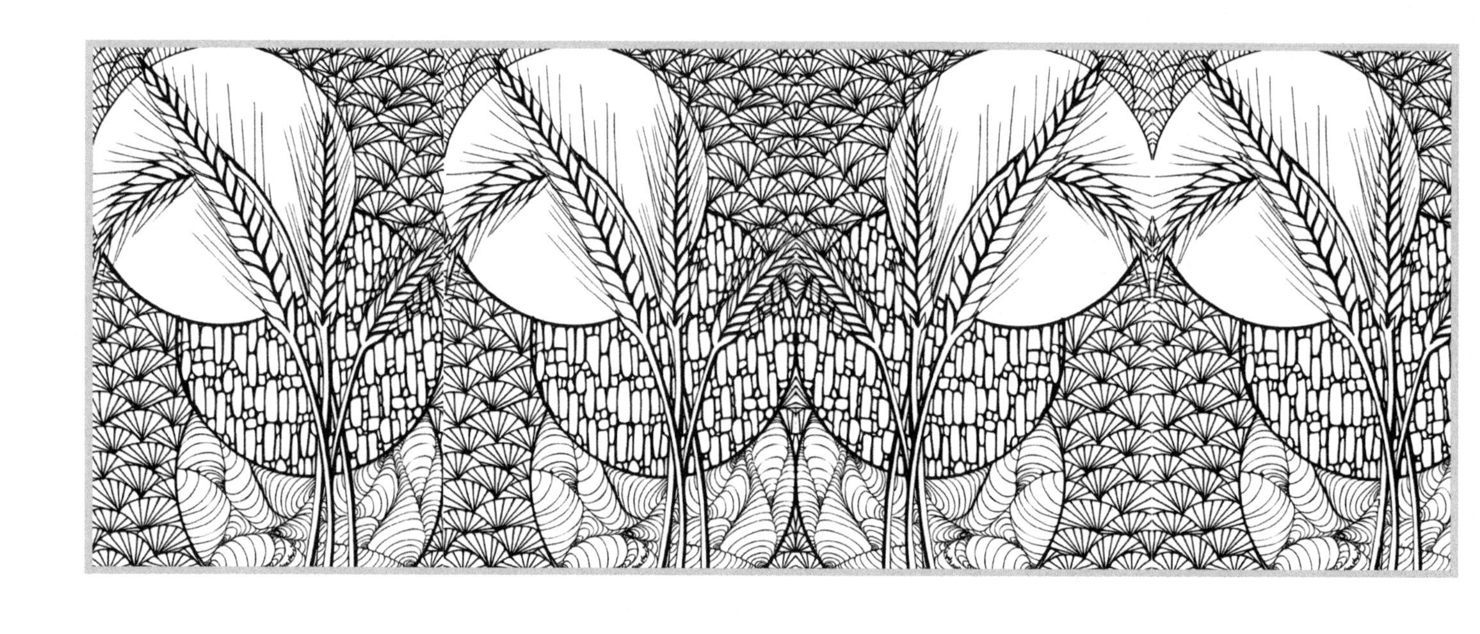

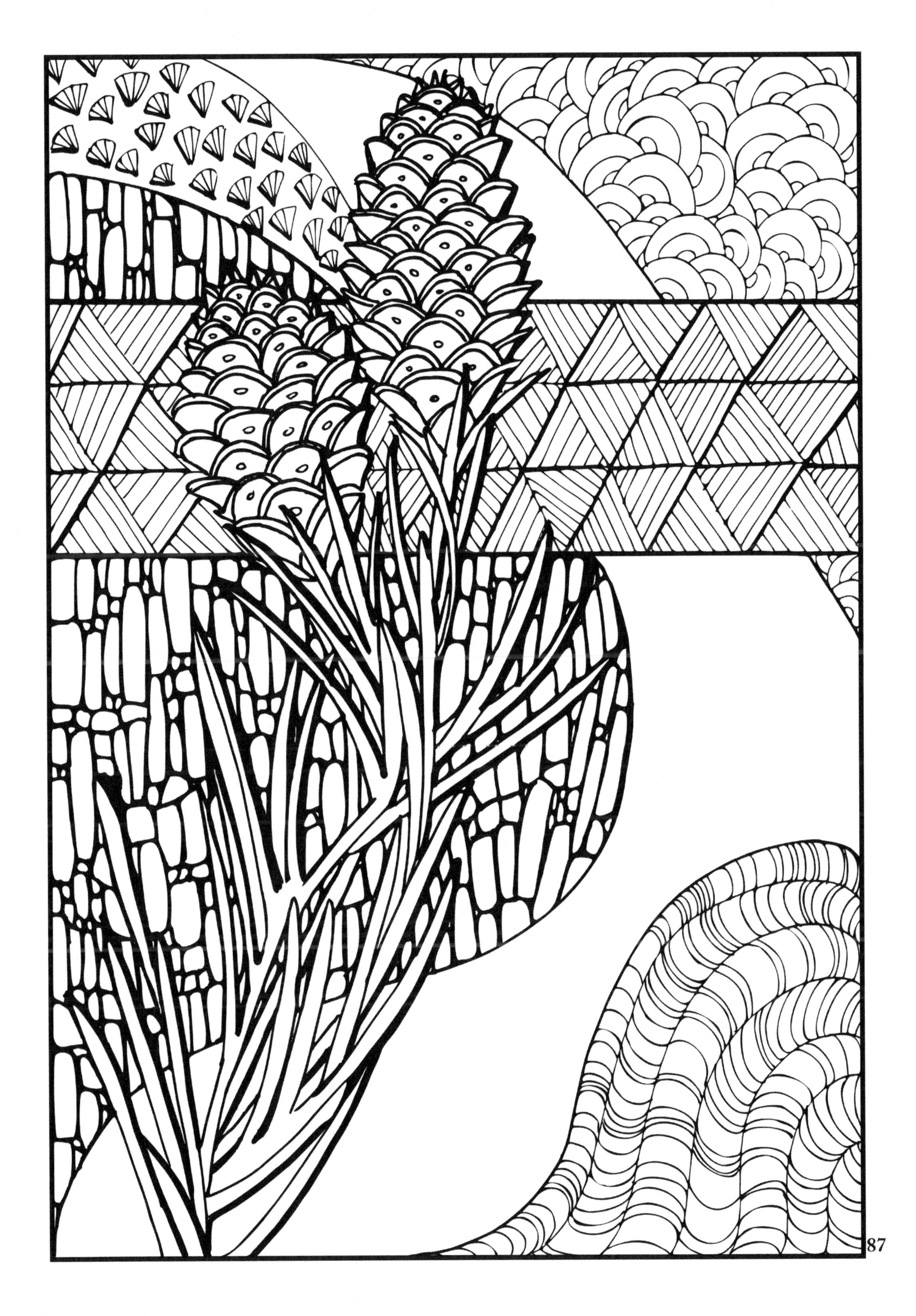

"While the earth remains,
Seedtime and harvest,
And cold and heat,
And summer and winter,
And day and night
Shall not cease."
Genesis 8:22

Good Seed

> ***"Jesus presented another parable to them, saying, 'The kingdom of heaven may be compared to a man who sowed good seed in his field.'"***
> ***Matthew 13:24***

We all sow bad seed, whether deliberately or inadvertently. Not a pleasant thought, is it? The continual bombardment of worldly opinion influences our decisions from the mundane to the weighty. In the chaos of our lives, creating a garden of peace, beauty, and abundance is possible if we sow God's Word. It is dynamic, fruitful seed. All else is bad seed. In order to garner the kind of harvest worth enjoying, distinguishing between the two and sowing good seed is crucial.

Instead of worrying about bad seed, let's linger on the excellence of good seed, which carries within it the power to do what you are unable to do. You can prepare the soil of your heart, but you cannot force germination or growth. Planting is, therefore, an act of faith in God, who alone possesses the power for growth and fruitfulness.

Time invested in studying, memorizing, thinking upon, and acting on God's Word is your sowing. His promises, instructions, and admonitions are mysterious seeds which, when mature, will lift you out of poverty, heal you, give you clarity, and empower you to thrive. He actively participates in causing your seed to sprout and bear fruit. Grace for every challenge will be available if His Word is sown in your heart. They are seeds to bless your present, your future, and your loved ones. These seeds will give you peace of mind, hope, and joy. They will bring dreams to life and keep you well cared for and protected! The seeds of God's Word are far more powerful than I can adequately describe in a few words.

In this coloring devotional journal, you've colored seeds that reflect only a smattering of the variety found in nature. The seed of God's Word is even more varied, sometimes encouraging and at other times correcting, and often offering a glimpse into your future. As the time to germinate is different for each natural seed, so also is the way they sprout. Variety is expressed in their every aspect—in leaves, shoots, stems, branches, and fruits. The only thing consistent about seeds is that they reproduce after their own kind—if you plant a kernel of corn, you won't be surprised by a plant with banana leaves that produces apples! So why would you expect a predictable sameness when you sow God's Word? Sometimes you will see remarkable results quickly, and at other times patience will be required of you.

The harvest of a single, carefully sown seed is not merely another seed. Hundreds, sometimes even thousands, of seeds can result from just one. It is not uncommon for fruit trees to yield hundreds of bushels of sweet fruit for years. That is why this is such a powerful principle: your harvest will be far greater than your wildest dreams! But it will require faith, patience, diligence, discipline, and active watchfulness.

Now You Know

"Now this I say, he who sows sparingly will also reap sparingly, and he who sows bountifully will also reap bountifully."

2 Corinthians 9:6

Are you poor in some area of life? Sow a seed. Think upon these promises from the Bible, which we've creatively absorbed in this journal. Now live as if they are true.

Do you feel you have nothing to sow? God says otherwise. He says that He ministers seed to the sower. Ask Him to show you the seed He has already given you. We are far richer than we realize.

Without sowing there is no harvest. Before you sow, make sure your ground is good soil. Then watch over your seed, water it, and be patient until it's time to harvest. Beware of wavering in doubt, and keep the weeds of skepticism pulled.

Sow deliberately the seed you intend to harvest. Do you lack time? Sow time into someone else's life. Need a friend? Be a friend. Hungry? Find someone to feed. Do you long for joy? Make someone smile. The world is a needy place, and answers to the longings of your heart are hidden in the principle of seedtime and harvest.

When we lack in some area of life, our natural inclination is to hoard our resources and spare nothing for another. Yielding to that impulse will keep you poor.

You can give your way out of poverty! There is no better way to experience the miraculous power of the seed than by emptying your precious stock and sowing it in faith. It will then be returned to you multiplied. You will find yourself growing rich in everything you once lacked. This has been God's way from the beginning of time.

Listen for His voice and obey. Sow when, and where, He prompts you, reaping when He tells you it's time to harvest. Trust that He will cause your seed to burst into life in the mysterious darkness of the earth.

Enjoy your harvest, but do not consume all your seed. Plant some for your future to continue the cycle of provision. Scatter your seed liberally and delight God, your provider, by this act of trust. Your life will then most certainly be jerked out of whatever rut you've been stuck in to speedily advance to a blessed future that is more than you could ever have imagined!

As you color your last page, think about the areas in your life that you would like to see change. Now plan your harvest in the next pages as methodically as a farmer plans his field, and record any actions you will take in faith. Be prayerfully deliberate as you write your plan.

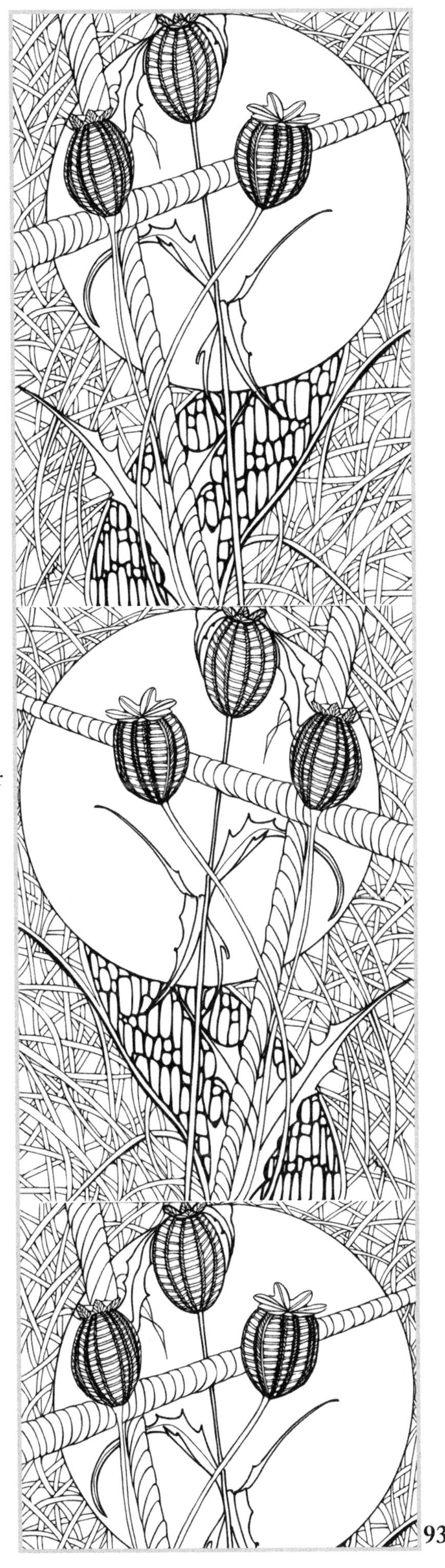

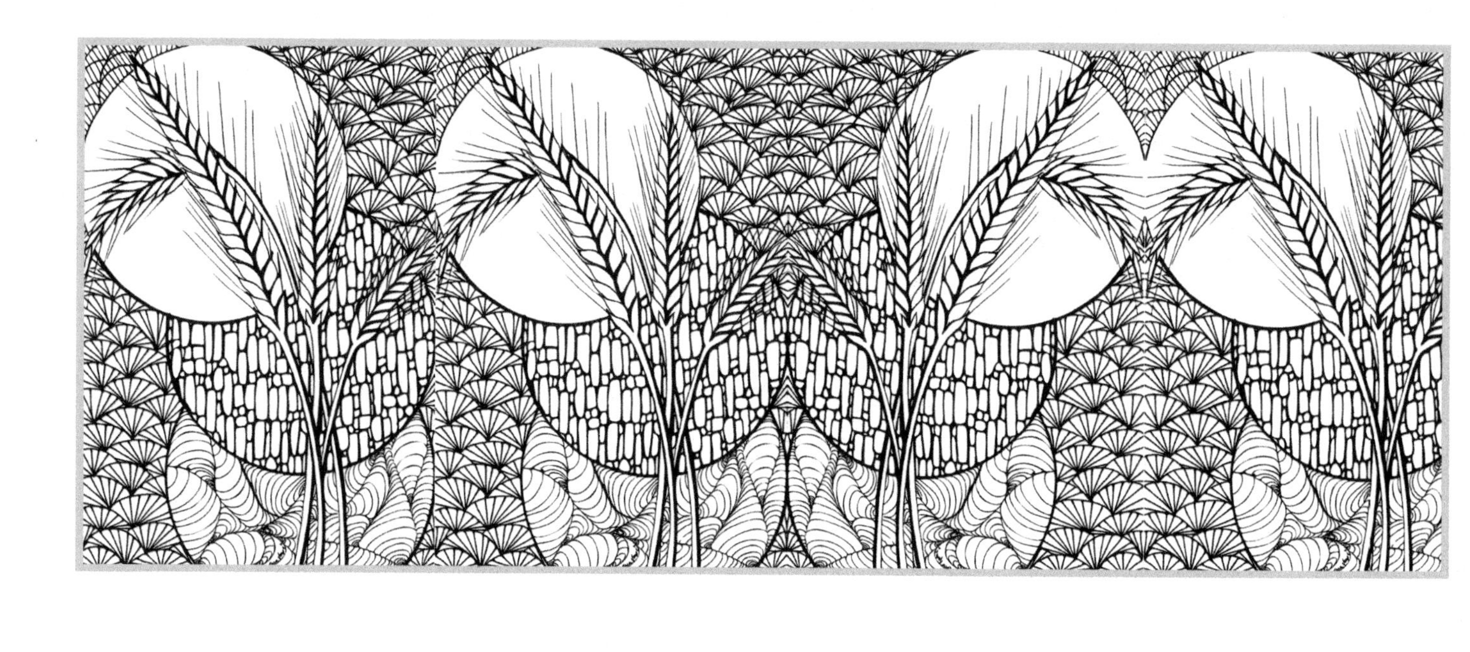

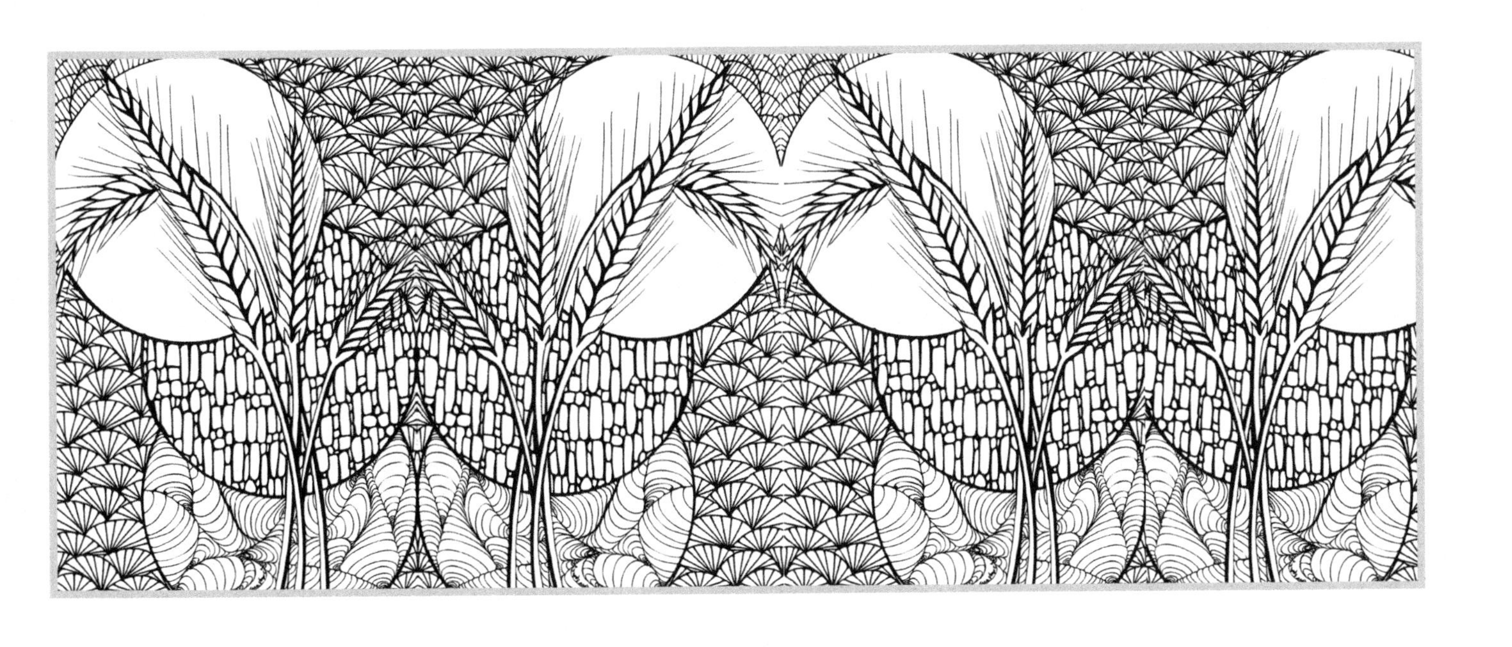

The End of This Journey, The Rest of Your Life

As you contemplate the power of the seed for the last time in this journal, I pray that you have anchored in your spirit these powerful truths from God's Word. Faith in His ability and desire to bless you is all you need to live victoriously. It is impossible to plumb the depths of the wisdom found in the principles of seedtime and harvest; trust God to teach you all you need to know.

Truth is always elegantly simple. Sow generously—first His Word in your heart, and then the things that it teaches in tangible actions of faith. Look to God for the harvest for every aspect of your life. As a witness to His unfailing love, I testify to His faithfulness.

What we perceive with our five senses tends to crowd out the spiritual reality of God's Word. Perhaps coloring so many seeds has reminded you of both the variety in nature as well as the variety in His Word, giving you insight on how to live. Choose to remember the lessons they so eloquently teach. In this journal, while thinking upon His words, you've engaged your visual and tactile senses as you colored. Some of those domineering senses were surely tamed by the truth.

I trust that your spirit is now stronger than when you began. When you falter in faith, may the Holy Spirit remind you of this journey.

Developing faith in God is priceless. Only when nurtured over time does it result in experiencing the kingdom that Jesus talks about. You've participated in that process by completing this coloring journal.

Real life is tough, but God can change those realities if you but trust Him to do so. May these truths that you have hidden in your heart remind you that to live abundantly you must sow richly and be a diligent harvester.

Thank you for joining me on this journey. I hope you've learned much and enjoyed the process.

If this book was a blessing to you, would you please consider rating and reviewing it on www.amazon.com and www.goodreads.com? I would be most grateful.

About the Author

Sara Joseph is a painter, sculptor, and writer. Her art, created in watercolor, ink, oils, acrylic, and polymer clay, is found in numerous corporate and private collections around the world.

Her early art training in India, the land of her birth, exposed Sara to the artistic traditions and rigor of the East. She immigrated to the United States with her husband, Jacob, and raised two sons, Johann and Reuben. A resident of Fort Worth, Texas, she is the author of the Christian Artist Resource website, an online resource for Christian artists internationally as well as a changing gallery of her own contemporary Christian art.

"Regardless of the medium I use," she says, "if the content is without meaning, I feel I've missed an opportunity that I may never get again—an opportunity to testify to the love of Jesus, the goodness of God, and the power of the Holy Spirit."

Her book, ***Gently Awakened: The Influence of Faith on Your Artistic Journey,*** was the 2014 Readers' Favorite International Book Award Gold Medal Winner for Christian Nonfiction and Illustration.

It is available on the Christian Artist Resource website, Amazon, Barnes and Noble, and other retail bookstores.

Visit her at www.christian-artist-resource.com to view her art and to stay informed about her latest projects.

Reviews

"Gently Awakened *converts the hearts of readers as it covers deep terrain of faith, theology, salvation, beauty, and creativity in an engaging and personal manner. This is a book that needed to be written and should be widely read.*" Marisa Martin, columnist, *World Net Daily*; visual artist

"This beautifully crafted book, illustrated in more ways than one with her own works, is an encouragement to recognize art in all its many forms as a divine calling." Linda Caddick

"Wow! I just got mine in the mail and just let me say ... this is so much more than an adult coloring book! Sara includes a devotional study of Luke's passage, as well as prayers, poems, and creative prompts for journaling! In addition, the designs to color are beautiful." Jody T

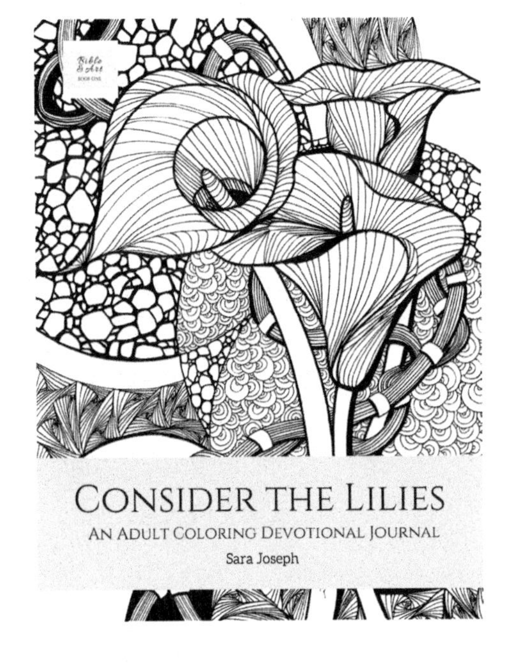

CPSIA information can be obtained
at www.ICGtesting.com
Printed in the USA
FSOW04n1338121117
41086FS

9 780997 367324